RESPONSES

Everyday Use
and other stories

KT-449-590

ELAINE MILLARD AND BARBARA WHITE

Nelson

Thomas Nelson and Sons Ltd
Nelson House Mayfield Road
Walton-on-Thames Surrey
KT12 5PL UK

51 York Place
Edinburgh
EH1 3JD UK

Thomas Nelson (Hong Kong) Ltd
Toppan Building 10/F
22A Westlands Road
Quarry Bay Hong Kong

Distributed in Australia by

Thomas Nelson Australia
480 La Trobe Street
Melbourne Victoria 3000
and in Sydney, Brisbane, Adelaide and Perth

© Elaine Millard and Barbara White 1990

First published by Thomas Nelson and Sons Ltd 1990
ISBN 0-17-432225-9
NPN 9 8 7 6 5 4 3 2 1

Printed and bound in Hong Kong

All Rights Reserved. No paragraph of this publication may be reproduced, copied or transmitted save with written permission or in accordance with the provisions of the Copyright, Design and Patents Act 1988, or under the terms of any licence permitting limited copying issued by the Copyright Licensing Agency, 33–34 Alfred Place, London WC1E 7DP

Any person who does any unauthorised act in relation to this publication may be liable to criminal prosecution and civil claims for damages

║ R E S P O N S E S ║

Series editors: Angel and Patrick Scott

Community Writing by Don Shiach
Frankie Mae and other stories by Ann Mann and Hilary Rich
Wordlife by Richard Knott
Everyday Use and other stories by Elaine Millard and
Barbara White
The Wild Bunch and other plays by Don Shiach
Diaries, Journals and Letters by Angel Scott

Editors' note
GCSE reflects the most interesting and successful initiatives in
English teaching that have taken place over the last 15 to 20 years.
As a consequence it is no longer possible to ignore classroom talk,
or to pretend that 'response' doesn't play an important part in
reading, and 'variety' in writing. No longer can the English curriculum
be sliced up into lessons on 'comprehension' or 'essay writing' or
'spelling'; the constituent parts of the subject are 'clearly inter-related
and interdependent' (National Criteria for GCSE) and one activity has
to grow naturally out of another.

The series builds on these principles. It aims to make available for
pupils some of the best contemporary sources ranging from familiar
literary genres, like poetry or the short story, to less conventional
forms, like community writing. The 'follow-on' work that is included at
the back of each book suggests ways in which the material might be
used to provoke discussion, develop ideas for folios of work and
introduce new ways of reading texts. That is why the series as a
whole is called '*Responses*'.

Angel and Patrick Scott

■ INTRODUCTION ■

From the many short stories we have shared with our classes, we have chosen those that we think are less well-known to others, but which have given us and our classes pleasure and stimulated a creative as well as a more critical response. The stories explore a wide variety of themes and range across a broad spectrum of cultural experience from courtship and marriage in Pakistan to childhood friendships in Wales, Ireland and the Caribbean. The main focus is on the richness and variety of ordinary lives. The wide range of contexts will encourage readers to empathise with experiences very different from their own. These stories capture both the essence of individual experiences while creating the distinctive atmosphere of a particular place at a particular time.

Modern fiction often focuses on serious and important issues in a challenging way that offers no ready or easy solutions. Many of the stories in this collection present failure or difficulties in communication between individuals, across generations or as a result of cultural differences. We have also found stories with a lighter touch that will both delight and entertain the reader.

Some of the stories lead the reader away from real to imaginary worlds. Damon Runyon's 'A Piece of Pie', creates a picture of American gangsters that is far removed from the world of violent crime portrayed on television; Terry Jones offers a contemporary moral fable in 'The Glass Cupboard'; Liz Lochhead's alternative fairy story, 'Rapunzstiltskin', which mixes two traditional tales, questions the common assumptions of fairy tales. We found our pupils enjoyed imitating the inventive ways of story-telling used by these writers.

Other stories in the collection deal with difficult decisions or issues which can be most successfully discussed in class through the mediation of a good story. Nadine Gordimer's story 'A Chip of Glass Ruby' gives an insight into the way in which apartheid affects the family life of races other than black Africans. Elizabeth Taylor's chilling tale, 'The Fly-paper', with its frightening twist, provides not only a narrative model for creating suspense, but also a way into discussing how children might be alerted to the possible dangers from strangers. On a different note, Garrison Keillor's story, 'Don: the True Story of a Young Person', explores pop culture and also raises important issues about the influence of the media, particularly the popular press, on ordinary lives.

Many of the stories are narrated by, or told from, the point of view of a young person and provide a narrative style which can be imitated or adapted to the experience of pupils studying for GCSE.

Although each of the stories we have chosen stands on its own, we have sometimes recommended research activities or class discussions to help the reader understand the background to a particular story. This is paricularly relevant to stories like 'Stench of Kerosene' and 'Everyday Use' which are set on other continents and involve different cultural expectations.

Inevitably one story leads to another and all new stories are enriched by aspects of ones we have previously read. In the wider reading we have suggested some stories which lead on from those we have chosen for this anthology. We have also recommended other stories and novels that can be used for the wider reading assignments expected for English courses.

The 'follow-on' section suggests a variety of activities for individual and group work. The questions range from discussion points which help focus attention on individual stories, to questions about how the stories are told and their effect upon the reader, through to suggestions for writing projects that require a personal response. These are, of course, only our ideas. We are sure teachers and pupils will find many more ways to share the stories with each other and to create opportunities for both talking and writing.

■ ACKNOWLEDGEMENTS ■

The authors and publishers are grateful to the following for permission to reproduce copyright material:

David Higham Associates Ltd for 'Everyday Use' © Alice Walker; Jonathan Cape Ltd for 'A Chip of Glass Ruby' © Nadime Gordimer; Longman Group Ltd for 'Snowdrops' © Leslie Norris; Virago and Elizabeth Taylor for 'Fly-Paper'; Faber and Faber Ltd for 'Don: The True Story of a Young Person' from *Happy To Be Here* © Garrison Keillor; Constable Publishers for 'Piece of Pie' from *Runyon Broadway* by Damon Runyon; Women's Press Ltd for 'Gorilla My Love' by Toni Cade Bambara – first published by Women's Press, London 1984; Edinburgh University Press and Liz Lochhead for 'Rapunzstiltskin'; Andre Deutsch Ltd for 'The Day they Burned the Books' from *Tigers are Better Looking* © Jean Rhys; Pavilion for 'The Glass Cupboard' © Terry Jones; A M Heath for 'Looking at Quilts' from *Living in the Open* © Marge Piercy; Macmillan Publishers Ltd and the estate of Walter Macken for 'Jane is a Girl' from *Doll Coll*.

We are unable to trace the copyright holders of 'Stench of Kerosene' by Anita Pritam and would appreciate any information which would help us to do so.

Every effort has been made to contact the holders of copyright material but if any have been inadvertently overlooked the publishers will be pleased to make the necessary arrangements at the first opportunity.

We wish to thank the colleagues in our institutions past and present who have worked with us in developing ideas and contributing to our knowledge about books and the way pupils respond to them; with special thanks to our school librarians who have been particularly helpful in resourcing our teaching.

Elaine Millard and Barbara White

■ CONTENTS ■

Everyday Use	Alice Walker	1
A Chip of Glass Ruby	Nadine Gordimer	11
Stench of Kerosene	Amrita Pritam	21
Snowdrops	Leslie Norris	27
The Fly-paper	Elizabeth Taylor	35
Jane is a Girl	Walter Macken	43
Don: the True Story of a Young Person	Garrison Keillor	49
A Piece of Pie	Damon Runyon	63
Gorilla, My Love	Toni Cade Bambara	78
Rapunzstiltskin	Liz Lochhead	85
The Glass Cupboard	Terry Jones	88
The Day They Burned the Books	Jean Rhys	92

Follow on

Before you start	100
Follow-on material:	101
Working with the story	
Reading between the lines	
Leaving the story behind	
Wider reading	
Working with the anthology	128
Analysis sheet	130
The hot seat	131
Activity map	133

Autobiographical fragments

We have suggested that you use several of the stories as a stimulus for your own memories. Collect together any of the pieces you have written as autobiographical fragments and rework them into a final longer piece of autobiography.

Everyday Use

■ *by Alice Walker* ■

for your grandmama

I will wait for her in the yard that Maggie and I made so clean and wavy yesterday afternoon. A yard like this is more comfortable than most people know. It is not just a yard. It is like an extended living-room. When the hard clay is swept clean as a floor and the fine sand around the edges lined with tiny, irregular grooves, anyone can come and sit and look up into the elm tree and wait for the breezes that never come inside the house.

Maggie will be nervous until after her sister goes: she will stand hopelessly in corners, homely and ashamed of the burn scars down her arms and legs, eyeing her sister with a mixture of envy and awe. She thinks her sister has held life always in the palm of one hand, that 'no' is a word the world never learned to say to her.

You've no doubt seen those TV shows where the child who has 'made it' is confronted, as a surprise, by her own mother and father, tottering in weakly from backstage. (A pleasant surprise, of course: what would they do if parent and child came on the show only to curse out and insult each other?) On TV mother and child embrace and smile into each other's faces. Sometimes the mother and father weep, the child wraps them in her arms and leans across the table to tell how she would not have made it without their help. I have seen these programmes.

Sometimes I dream a dream in which Dee and I are suddenly brought together on a TV programme of this sort. Out of a dark and soft-seated limousine I am ushered into a bright room filled with many people. There I meet a smiling, grey, sporty man like Johnny Carson who shakes my hand and tells me what a fine girl I have. Then we are on the stage and Dee is embracing me with tears in her eyes. She pins on my dress a large orchid, even though she has told me once that she thinks orchids are tacky flowers.

In real life I am a large, big-boned woman with rough, man-working hands. In the winter I wear flannel night-gowns to bed and overalls during the day. I can kill and clean a hog as mercilessly as a man. My fat keeps me hot in zero weather. I can work outside all day, breaking ice to get water for washing; I can eat pork liver cooked over the open fire minutes after it comes steaming from the hog. One winter I knocked a bull calf straight in the brain between the eyes with a sledge hammer and had the meat hung up to chill before nightfall. But of course all this does not show on television. I am the way my daughter would want me to be: a hundred pounds lighter, my skin like an uncooked barley

2

pancake. My hair glistens in the hot bright lights. Johnny Carson has much to do to keep up with my quick and witty tongue.

But that is a mistake. I know even before I wake up. Who ever knew a Johnson with a quick tongue? Who can even imagine me looking a strange white man in the eye? It seems to me I have talked to them always with one foot raised in flight, with my head turned in whichever way is farthest from them. Dee, though. She would always look anyone in the eye. Hesitation was no part of her nature.

'How do I look, Mama?' Maggie says, showing just enough of her thin body enveloped in pink skirt and red blouse for me to know she's there, almost hidden by the door.

'Come out into the yard,' I say.

Have you ever seen a lame animal, perhaps a dog run over by some careless person rich enough to own a car, sidle up to someone who is ignorant enough to be kind to him? That is the way my Maggie walks. She has been like this, chin on chest, eyes on ground, feet in shuffle, ever since the fire that burned the other house to the ground.

Dee is lighter than Maggie, with nicer hair and a fuller figure. She's a woman now, though sometimes I forget. How long ago was it that the other house burned? Ten, twelve years? Sometimes I can still hear the flames and feel Maggie's arms sticking to me, her hair smoking and her dress falling off her in little black papery flakes. Her eyes seemed stretched open, blazed open by the flames reflected in them. And Dee. I see her standing off under the sweet gum tree she used to dig gum out of: a look of concentration on her face as she watched the last dingy grey board of the house fall in toward the red-hot brick chimney. Why don't you do a dance around the ashes? I'd wanted to ask her. She had hated the house that much.

I used to think she hated Maggie, too. But that was before we raised the money, the church and me, to send her to Augusta to school. She used to read to us without pity; forcing words, lies, other folks' habits, whole lives upon us two, sitting trapped and ignorant underneath her voice. She washed us in a river of make believe, burned us with a lot of knowledge we didn't necessarily need to know. Pressed us to her with the serious way she read, to shove us away at just the moment, like dimwits, we seemed about to understand.

Dee wanted nice things. A yellow organdie dress to wear to her graduation from high school; black pumps to match a green suit she'd made from an old suit somebody gave me. She was determined to stare down any disaster in her efforts. Her eyelids would not flicker for minutes at a time. Often I fought off the temptation to shake her. At sixteen she had a style of her own: and knew what style was.

I never had an education myself. After second grade the school was closed down. Don't ask me why: in 1927 coloured asked fewer questions than they do now. Sometimes Maggie reads to me. She stumbles along good-naturedly but can't see well. She knows she is not bright. Like good looks and money, quickness passed her by. She will marry John Thomas (who has mossy teeth in an earnest face) and then I'll be free to sit here and I guess just sing church songs to myself. Although I never was a good singer. Never could carry a tune. I was always better at a man's job. I used to love to milk till I was hooked in the side in '49. Cows are soothing and slow and don't bother you, unless you try to milk them the wrong way.

I have deliberately turned my back on the house. It is three rooms, just like the one that burned, except the roof is tin; they don't make shingle roofs any more. There are no real windows, just some holes cut in the sides, like the portholes in a ship, but not round and not square, with rawhide holding the shutters up on the outside. This house is in a pasture, too, like the other one. No doubt when Dee sees it she will want to tear it down. She wrote me once that no matter where we 'choose' to live, she will manage to come see us. But she will never bring her friends. Maggie and I thought about this and Maggie asked me, 'Mama, when did Dee ever *have* any friends?'

She had a few. Furtive boys in pink shirts hanging about on washday after school. Nervous girls who never laughed. Impressed with her they worshipped the well-turned phrase, the cute shape, the scalding humour that erupted like bubbles in lye. She read to them.

When she was courting Jimmy T she didn't have much time to pay to us, but turned all her faultfinding power on him. He *flew* to marry a cheap city girl from a family of ignorant flashy people. She hardly had time to recompose herself.

When she comes I will meet – but there they are!

Maggie attempts to make a dash for the house, in her shuffling way, but I stay her with my hand. 'Come back here,' I say. And she stops and tries to dig a well in the sand with her toe.

4

It is hard to see them clearly through the strong sun. But even the first glimpse of leg out of the car tells me it is Dee. Her feet were always neat-looking, as if God himself had shaped them with a certain style. From the other side of the car comes a short, stocky man. Hair is all over his head a foot long and hanging from his chin like a kinky mule tail. I hear Maggie suck in her breath. 'Uhnnnh', is what it sounds like. Like when you see the wriggling end of a snake just in front of your foot on the road. 'Uhnnnh.'

Dee next. A dress down to the ground, in this hot weather. A dress so loud it hurts my eyes. There are yellows and oranges enough to throw back the light of the sun. I feel my whole face warming from the heat waves it throws out. Earrings gold, too, and hanging down to her shoulders. Bracelets dangling and making noises when she moves her arm up to shake the folds of the dress out of her armpits. The dress is loose and flows, and as she walks closer, I like it. I hear Maggie go 'Uhnnnh' again. It is her sister's hair. It stands straight up like the wool on a sheep. It is black as night and around the edges are two long pigtails that rope about like small lizards disappearing behind her ears.

'Wa-su-zo-Tean-o!' she says, coming on in that gliding way the dress makes her move. The short stocky fellow with the hair to his navel is all grinning and he follows up with 'Asalamalakim, my mother and sister!' He moves to hug Maggie but she falls back, right up against the back of my chair. I feel her trembling there and when I look up I see the perspiration falling off her chin.

'Don't get up,' says Dee. Since I am stout it takes something of a push. You can see me trying to move a second or two before I make it. She turns, showing white heels through her sandals, and goes back to the car. Out she peeks next with a Polaroid. She stoops down quickly and lines up picture after picture of me sitting there in front of the house with Maggie cowering behind me. She never takes a shot without making sure the house is included. When a cow comes nibbling around the edge of the yard she snaps it and me and Maggie *and* the house. Then she puts the Polaroid in the back seat of the car, and comes up and kisses me on the forehead.

Meanwhile Asalamalakim is going through motions with Maggie's hand. Maggie's hand is as limp as a fish, and probably as cold, despite the sweat, and she keeps trying to pull it back. It looks like Asalamalakim wants to shake hands but wants to do it fancy. Or maybe he don't know how people shake hands. Anyhow, he soon gives up on Maggie.

'Well,' I say. ' "Dee".'

'No, Mama,' she says. 'Not "Dee," Wangero Leewanika Kemanjo!'

'What happened to "Dee"?' I wanted to know.

'She's dead,' Wangero said. 'I couldn't bear it any longer, being named after the people who oppress me.'

'You know as well as me you was named after your aunt Dicie,' I said. Dicie is my sister. She named Dee. We called her 'Big Dee' after Dee was born.

'But who was *she* named after?' asked Wangero.

'I guess after Grandma Dee,' I said.

'And who was she named after?' asked Wangero.

'Her mother,' I said, and saw Wangero was getting tired. 'That's about as far back as I can trace it,' I said. Though, in fact, I probably could have carried it back beyond the Civil War through the branches.

'Well,' said Asalamalakim, 'there you are.'

'Uhnnnh,' I heard Maggie say.

'There I was not,' I said, 'before "Dicie" cropped up in our family, so why should I try to trace it that far back?'

He just stood there grinning, looking down on me like somebody inspecting a Model A car. Every once in a while he and Wangero sent eye signals over my head.

'How do you pronounce this name?' I asked.

'You don't have to call me by it if you don't want to,' said Wangero.

'Why shouldn't I?' I asked. 'If that's what you want us to call you, we'll call you.'

'I know it might sound awkward at first,' said Wangero.

'I'll get used to it,' I said. 'Ream it out again.'

Well, soon we got the name out of the way. Asalamalakim had a name twice as long and three times as hard. After I tripped over it two or three times he told me to just call him Hakim-a-barber. I wanted to ask him was he a barber, but I didn't really think he was, so I didn't ask.

'You must belong to those beef-cattle peoples down the road,' I said. They said 'Asalamalakim' when they met you, too, but they didn't shake hands. Always too busy: feeding the cattle, fixing the fences, putting up salt-lick shelters, throwing down hay. When the white folks poisoned some of the herd the men stayed

6

up all night with rifles in their hands. I walked a mile and a half just to see the sight.

Hakim-a-barber said, 'I accept some of their doctrines, but farming and raising cattle is not my style.' (They didn't tell me, and I didn't ask, whether Wangero [Dee] had really gone and married him.)

We sat down to eat and right away he said he didn't eat collards and pork was unclean. Wangero, though, went on through the chitlins and corn bread, the greens and everything else. She talked a blue streak over the sweet potatoes. Everything delighted her. Even the fact that we still used the benches her daddy made for the table when we couldn't afford to buy chairs.

'Oh, Mama!' she cried. Then turned to Hakim-a-barber 'I never knew how lovely these benches are. You can feel the rump prints,' she said, running her hands underneath her and along the bench. Then she gave a sigh and her hand closed over Grandma Dee's butter dish. 'That's it!' she said, 'I knew there was something I wanted to ask you if I could have.' She jumped up from the table and went over in the corner where the churn stood, the milk in it clabber by now. She looked at the churn and looked at it.

'This churn top is what I need,' she said. 'Didn't Uncle Buddy whittle it out of a tree you all used to have?'

'Yes,' I said.

'Uh huh,' she said happily. 'And I want the dasher, too.'

'Uncle Buddy whittle that, too?' asked the barber.

Dee (Wangero) looked up at me.

'Aunt Dee's first husband whittled the dash,' said Maggie so low you almost couldn't hear her. 'His name was Henry, but they called him Stash.'

'Maggie's brain is like an elephant's,' Wangero said, laughing. 'I can use the churn top as a centrepiece for the alcove table,' she said, sliding a plate over the churn, 'and I'll think of something artistic to do with the dasher.'

When she finished wrapping the dasher the handle stuck out. I took it for a moment in my hands. You didn't even have to look close to see where hands pushing the dasher up and down to make butter had left a kind of sink in the wood. In fact, there were a lot of small sinks; you could see where thumbs and fingers had sunk into the wood. It was beautiful light yellow wood, from a tree that grew in the yard where Big Dee and Stash had lived.

After dinner Dee (Wangero) went to the trunk at the foot of my bed and started rifling through it. Maggie hung back in the kitchen over the dishpan. Out came Wangero with two quilts.

7

They had been pieced by Grandma Dee and then Big Dee and me had hung them on the quilt frames on the front porch and quilted them. One was in the Lone Star pattern. The other was Walk Around the Mountain. In both of them were scraps of dresses Grandma Dee had worn fifty and more years ago. Bits and pieces of Grandpa Jarrell's Paisley shirts. And one teeny faded blue piece, about the size of a penny matchbox, that was from Great Grandpa Ezra's uniform that he wore in the Civil War.

'Mama,' Wangero said sweet as a bird. 'Can I have these old quilts?'

I heard something fall in the kitchen, and a minute later the kitchen door slammed.

'Why don't you take one or two of the others?' I asked. 'These old things was just done by me and Big Dee from some tops your grandma pieced before she died.'

'No,' said Wangero. 'I don't want those. They are stitched around the borders by machine.'

'That'll make them last better,' I said.

'That's not the point,' said Wangero. 'These are all pieces of dresses Grandma used to wear. She did all this stitching by hand. Imagine!' She held the quilts securely in her arms, stroking them.

'Some of the pieces, like those lavender ones, come from old clothes her mother handed down to her,' I said, moving up to touch the quilts. Dee (Wangero) moved back just enough so that I couldn't reach the quilts. They already belonged to her.

'Imagine!' she breathed again, clutching them closely to her bosom.

'The truth is,' I said, 'I promised to give them quilts to Maggie, for when she marries John Thomas.'

She gasped like a bee had stung her.

'Maggie can't appreciate these quilts!' she said. 'She'd probably be backward enough to put them to everyday use.'

'I reckon she would,' I said. 'God knows I been saving 'em for long enough with nobody using 'em. I hope she will!' I didn't want to bring up how I had offered Dee (Wangero) a quilt when she went away to college. Then she had told me they were old-fashioned, out of style.

'But they're *priceless*!' she was saying now, furiously; for she has a temper. 'Maggie would put them on the bed and in five years they'd be in rags. Less than that!'

'She can always make some more,' I said. 'Maggie knows how to quilt.'

Dee (Wangero) looked at me with hatred. 'You just will not understand. The point is these quilts, *these* quilts!'

'Well,' I said, stumped. 'What would *you* do with them?'

'Hang them,' she said. As if that was the only thing you *could* do with quilts.

Maggie by now was standing in the door. I could almost hear the sound her feet made as they scraped over each other.

'She can have them, Mama,' she said, like somebody used to never winning anything, or having anything reserved for her. 'I can 'member Grandma Dee without the quilts.'

I looked at her hard. She had filled her bottom lip with checker-berry snuff and it gave her face a kind of dopey, hangdog look. It was Grandma Dee and Big Dee who taught her how to quilt herself. She stood there with her scarred hands hidden in the folds of her skirt. She looked at her sister with something like fear but she wasn't mad at her. This was Maggie's portion. This was the way she knew God to work.

When I looked at her like that something hit me in the top of my head and ran down to the soles of my feet. Just like when I'm in church and the spirit of God touches me and I get happy and shout. I did something I never had done before: hugged Maggie to me, then dragged her on into the room, snatched the quilts out of Miss Wangero's hands and dumped them into Maggie's lap. Maggie just sat there on my bed with her mouth open.

'Take one or two of the others,' I said to Dee.

But she turned without a word and went out to Hakim-a-barber.

'You just don't understand,' she said, as Maggie and I came out to the car.

'What don't I understand?' I wanted to know.

'Your heritage,' she said. And then she turned to Maggie, kissed her, and said, 'You ought to try to make something of yourself, too, Maggie. It's really a new day for us. But from the way you and Mama still live you'd never know it.'

She put on some sunglasses that hid everything above the tip of her nose and her chin.

Maggie smiled; maybe at the sunglasses. But a real smile, not scared. After we watched the car dust settle I asked Maggie to bring me a dip of snuff. And then the two of us sat there just enjoying, until it was time to go in the house and go to bed.

Alice Walker is a black American poet, novelist and essay writer, who has received a number of literary awards for her work, including a Guggenheim Fellowship and a Pulitzer prize. She was born in Eatonton, Georgia, the daughter of a share-cropper (a tenant farmer who pays the landowner by giving him a share of his crops). She now lives in San Fransisco.

She has published two collections of short stories, *In Love and Trouble* (1984) and *You Can't Keep a Good Woman Down* (1982), which explore the prejudices of modern America. Her collections of poetry are: *Once* (1986), *Revolutionary Petunias, Good Night, Willie Lee, I'll see you in the Morning* and *Horses Make a Landscape Look More Beautiful* (1985). *The Color Purple* (1983), the best known of her novels, has also been adapted as a film directed by Stephen Speilberg.

A Chip of Glass Ruby

■ *by Nadine Gordimer* ■

When the duplicating machine was brought into the house, Bamjee said, 'Isn't it enough that you've got the Indians' troubles on your back?' Mrs Bamjee said, with a smile that showed the gap of a missing tooth but was confident all the same, 'What's the difference, Yusuf? We've all got the same troubles.'

'Don't tell me that. We don't have to carry passes; let the natives protest against passes on their own, there are millions of them. Let them go ahead with it.'

The nine Bamjee and Pahad children were present at this exchange as they were always; in the small house that held them all there was no room for privacy for the discussion of matters they were too young to hear, and so they had never been too young to hear anything. Only their sister and half-sister, Girlie, was missing; she was the eldest, and married. The children looked expectantly, unalarmed and interested, at Bamjee, who had neither left the room nor settled down again to the task of rolling his own cigarettes, which had been interrupted by the arrival of the duplicator. He had looked at the thing that had come hidden in a wash-basket and conveyed in a black man's taxi, and the children turned on it too, their black eyes surrounded by thick lashes like those still, open flowers with hairy tentacles that close on whatever touches them.

'A fine thing to have on the table where we eat,' was all he said at last. They smelled the machine among them; a smell of cold black grease. He went out, heavily on tiptoe, in his troubled way.

'It's going to go nicely on the sideboard!' Mrs Bamjee was busy making a place by removing the two pink glass vases filled with plastic carnations and the hand-painted velvet runner with the picture of the Taj Mahal.

After supper she began to run off leaflets on the machine. The family lived in that room – the three other rooms in the house were full of beds – and they were all there. The older children shared a bottle of ink while they did their homework, and the two little ones pushed a couple of empty milk-bottles in and out the chair-legs. The three-year-old fell asleep and was carted away by one of the girls. They all drifted off to bed eventually; Bamjee himself went before the older children – he was a fruit-and-vegetable hawker and was up at half past four every morning to get to the market by five. 'Not long now,' said Mrs Bamjee. The older children looked up and smiled at him. He turned his back on her. She still wore the traditional clothing of a Moslem woman, and her body, which was scraggy and unimportant as a dress on a peg when it was not host to a child, was wrapped in the trailing rags of a cheap sari and her thin black plait was greased. When she was a girl, in the Transvaal town where they lived still, her mother fixed a chip of glass ruby in her nostril; but she had abandoned that adornment as too old-style, even for her, long ago.

She was up until long after midnight, turing out leaflets. She did it as if she might have been pounding chillies.

Bamjee did not have to ask what the leaflets were. He had read the papers. All the past week Africans had been destroying their passes and then presenting themselves for arrest. Their leaders were jailed on charges of incitement, campaign offices were raided – someone must be helping the few minor leaders who were left to keep the campaign going without offices or equipment. What was it the leaflets would say – 'Don't go to work tomorrow', 'Day of Protest', 'Burn Your Pass for Freedom'? He didn't want to see.

He was used to coming home and finding his wife sitting at the table deep in discussion with strangers or people whose names were familiar by repute. Some were prominent Indians, like the lawyer, Dr Abdul Mohammed Khan, or the big businessman, Mr Moonsamy Patel, and he was flattered, in a suspicious way, to meet them in his house. As he came home from work next day he met Dr Khan coming out of the house and Dr Khan – a highly educated man – said to him, 'A wonderful woman.' But Bamjee had never caught his wife out in any presumption; she behaved properly, as any Moslem woman should, and once her business with such gentlemen was over would never, for instance, have sat down to eat with them. He found her now back in the kitchen, setting about the preparation of dinner and carrying on a conversation on several different wave-lengths with the children. 'It's really a shame if you're tired of lentils, Jimmy, because that's what you're getting – Amina, hurry up, get a pot of water going – don't worry, I'll mend that in a minute, just bring the yellow cotton, and there's a needle in the cigarette box on the sideboard.'

'Was that Dr Khan leaving?' said Bamjee.

'Yes, there's going to be a stay-at-home on Monday. Desai's ill, and he's got to get the word around by himself. Bob Jali was up all last night printing leaflets, but he's gone to have a tooth out.' She had always treated Bamjee as if it were only a mannerism that made him appear uninterested in politics, the way some woman will persist in interpreting her husband's bad temper as an endearing gruffness hiding boundless goodwill, and she talked

13

to him of these things just as she passed on to him neighbours' or family gossip.

'What for do you want to get mixed up with these killings and stonings and I don't know what? Congress should keep out of it. Isn't it enough with the Group Areas?'

She laughed. 'Now, Yusuf, you know you don't believe that. Look how you said the same thing when the Group Areas started in Natal. You said we should begin to worry when we get moved out of our own houses here in the Transvaal. And then your own mother lost her house in Noorddorp, and there you are; you saw that nobody's safe. Oh, Girlie was here this afternoon, she says Ismail's brother's engaged – that's nice, isn't it? His mother will be pleased; she was worried.'

'Why was she worried?' asked Jimmy, who was fifteen, and old enough to patronise his mother.

'Well, she wanted to see him settled. There's a party on Sunday week at Ismail's place – you'd better give me your suit to give to the cleaners tomorrow, Yusuf.'

One of the girls presented herself at once. 'I'll have nothing to wear, Ma.'

Mrs Bamjee scratched her sallow face. 'Perhaps Girlie will lend you her pink, eh? Run over to Girlie's place now and say I say will she lend it to you.'

The sound of commonplaces often does service as security, and Bamjee, going to sit in the armchair with the shiny arm-rests that was wedged between the table and the sideboard, lapsed into an unthinking doze that, like all times of dreamlike ordinariness during those weeks, was filled with uneasy jerks and starts back into reality. The next morning, as soon as he got to market, he heard that Dr Khan had been arrested. But that night Mrs Bamjee sat up making a new dress for her daughter; the sight disarmed Bamjee, reassured him again, against his will, so that the resentment he had been making ready all day faded into a morose and accusing silence. Heaven knew, of course, who came and went in the house during the day. Twice in that week of riots, raids and arrests, he found black women in the house when he came home; plain ordinary native women in docks, drinking tea. This was not a thing other Indian women would have in their homes, he thought bitterly; but then his wife was not like other people, in a way he could not put his finger on, except to say what it was not: not scandalous, not punishable, not rebellious. It was, like the attraction that had led him to marry her, Pahad's widow with five children, something he could not see clearly.

14

When the Special Branch knocked steadily on the door in the small hours of Thursday morning he did not wake up, for his return to consciousness was always set in his mind to half past four, and that was more than an hour away. Mrs Bamjee got up herself, struggled into Jimmy's raincoat which was hanging over a chair and went to the front door. The clock on the wall – a wedding present when she married Pahad – showed three o'clock when she snapped on the light, and she knew at once who it was on the other side of the door. Although she was not surprised, her hands shook like a very old person's as she undid the locks and the complicated catch on the wire burglar-proofing. And then she opened the door and they were there – two coloured policemen in plain clothes. 'Zanip Bamjee?'

'Yes.'

As they talked, Bamjee woke up in the sudden terror of having overslept. Then he became conscious of men's voices. He heaved himself out of bed in the dark and went to the window, which, like the front door, was covered with a heavy mesh of thick wire against intruders from the dingy lane it looked upon. Bewildered, he appeared in the room, where the policemen were searching through a soapbox of papers beside the duplicating machine. 'Yusuf, it's for me,' Mrs Bamjee said.

At once, the snap of a trap, realisation came. He stood there in an old shirt before the two policemen, and the woman was going off to prison because of the natives. 'There you are!' he shouted, standing away from her. 'That's what you've got for it. Didn't I tell you? Didn't I? That's the end of it now. That's the finish. That's what it's come to.' She listened with her head at the slightest tilt to one side, as if to ward off a blow, or in compassion.

Jimmy, Pahad's son, appeared at the door with a suitcase; two or three of the girls were behind him. 'Here, Ma, you take my green jersey.' 'I've found your clean blouse,' Bamjee had to keep moving out of their way as they helped their mother to make ready. It was like the preparation for one of the family festivals his wife made such a fuss over; wherever he put himself, they bumped into him. Even the two policemen mumbled, 'Excuse me,' and pushed past into the rest of the house to continue their search. They took with them a tome that Nehru had written in prison; it had been bought from a persevering travelling salesman and kept, for years, on the mantelpiece. 'Oh, don't take that, please,' Mrs Bamjee said suddenly, clinging to the arm of the man who had picked it up.

The man held it away from her.

'What does it matter, Ma?'

It was true that no one in the house had ever read it; but she said, 'It's for my children.'

'Ma, leave it,' Jimmy, who was squat and plump, looked like a merchant advising a client against a roll of silk she had set her heart on. She went into the bedroom and got dressed. When she came out in her old yellow sari with a brown coat over it, the faces of the children were behind her like faces on the platform of a railway station. They kissed her good-bye. The policemen did not hurry her, but she seemed to be in a hurry just the same.

'What am I going to do?' Bamjee accused them all.

The policemen looked away patiently.

'It'll be all right. Girlie will help. The big children can manage. And Yusuf –' The children crowded in around her; two of the younger ones had awakened and appeared, asking shrill questions.

'Come on,' said the policemen.

'I want to speak to my husband.' She broke away and came back to him, and the movement of her sari hid them from the rest of the room for a moment. His face hardened in suspicious anticipation against the request to give some message to the next fool who would take up her pamphleteering until he, too, was arrested. 'On Sunday,' she said. 'Take them on Sunday.' He did not know what she was talking about. 'The engagement party,' she whispered, low and urgent. 'They shouldn't miss it. Ismail will be offended.'

They listened to the car drive away. Jimmy bolted and barred the front door, and then at once opened it again; he put on the raincoat that his mother had taken off. 'Going to tell Girlie,' he said. The children went back to bed. Their father did not say a word to any of them; their talk, the crying of the younger ones and the argumentative voices of the older, went on in the bed-rooms. He found himself alone; he felt the night all around him. And then he happened to meet the clock face and saw with a terrible sense of unfamiliarity that this was not the secret night but an hour he should have recognised: the time he always got up. He pulled on his trousers and his dirty white hawker's coat and wound his grey muffler up to the stubble on his chin and went to work.

The duplicating machine was gone from the sideboard. The police-men had taken it with them, along with the pamphlets and the conference reports and the stack of old newspapers that had collected on top of the wardrobe in the bedroom – not the thick

16

dailies of the white men but the thin, impermanent-looking papers that spoke up, sometimes interrupted by suppression or lack of money, for the rest. It was all gone. When he had married her and moved in with her and her five children, into what had been the Pahad and became the Bamjee house, he had not recognised the humble, harmless and apparently useless routine tasks – the minutes of meetings being written up on the dining-room table at night, the government blue books that were read while the latest bady was suckled, the employment of the fingers of the older children in the fashioning of crinkle-paper Congress rosettes – as activity intended to move mountains. For years and years he had not noticed it, and now it was gone.

The house was quiet. The children kept to their lairs, crowded on the beds with the doors shut. He sat and looked at the sideboard, where the plastic carnations and the mat with the picture of the Taj Mahal were in place. For the first few weeks he never spoke of her. There was the feeling, in the house, that he had wept and raged at her, that boulders of reproach had thundered down upon her absence, and yet he had said not one word. He had not been to inquire where she was; Jimmy and Girlie had gone to Mohammed Ebrahim, the lawyer, and when he found out that their mother had been taken – when she was arrested, at least – to a prison in the next town, they had stood about outside the big prison door for hours while they waited to be told where she had been moved from there. At last they had discovered that she was fifty miles away, in Pretoria. Jimmy asked Bamjee for five shillings to help Girlie pay the train fare to Pretoria, once she had been interviewed by the police and had been given a permit to visit her mother; he put three two-shilling pieces on the table for Jimmy to pick up, and the boy, looking at him keenly, did not know whether the extra shilling meant anything, or whether it was merely that Bamjee had no change.

It was only when relations and neighbours came to the house that Bamjee would suddenly begin to talk. He had never been so expansive in his life as he was in the company of these visitors, many of them came on a polite call rather in the nature of a visit of condolence. 'Ah, yes, yes, you can see how I am – you see what has been done to me. Nine children, and I am on the cart all day. I get home at seven or eight. What are you to do? What can people like us do?'

'Poor Mrs Bamjee. Such a kind lady.'

'Well, you see for yourself. They walk in here in the middle of the night and leave a houseful of children. I'm out on the cart all day, I've got a living to earn.' Standing about in his shirt sleeves, he became quite animated; he would call for the girls to bring fruit drinks for the visitors. When they were gone, it was as if he, who was orthodox if not devout and never drank liquor, had been drunk and abruptly sobered up; he looked dazed and could not have gone over in his mind what he had been saying. And as he cooled, the lump of resentment and wrongedness stopped his throat again.

Bamjee found one of the little boys the centre of a self-important group of championing brothers and sisters in the room one evening. 'They've been cruel to Ahmed.'

'What has he done?' said the father.

'Nothing! Nothing!' The little girl stood twisting her handkerchief excitedly.

An older one, thin as her mother, took over, silencing the others with a gesture of her skinny hand. 'They did it at school today. They made an example of him.'

'What is an example?' said Bamjee impatiently.

'The teacher made him come up and stand in front of the whole class, and he told them, "You see this boy? His mother's in jail because she likes the natives so much. She wants the Indians to be the same as natives."'

'It's terrible,' he said. His hands fell to his sides. 'Did she ever think of this?'

'That's why Ma's *there*,' said Jimmy, putting aside his comic and emptying out his schoolbooks upon the table. 'That's all the kids need to know. Ma's there because things like this happen. Petersen's a coloured teacher, and it's his black blood that's brought him trouble all his life, I suppose. He hates anyone who says everybody's the same because that takes away from him his bit of whiteness that's all he's got. What d'you expect? It's nothing to make too much fuss about.'

'Of course, you are fifteen and you know everything.' Bamjee mumbled at him.

'I don't say that. But I know Ma, anyway.' The boy laughed.

There was a hunger strike among the political prisoners, and Bamjee could not bring himself to ask Girlie if her mother was starving herself too. He would not ask; and yet he saw in the young woman's face the gradual weakening of her mother. When the strike had gone on for nearly a week one of the elder children burst into tears at the table and could not eat. Bamjee pushed his own plate away in rage.

Sometimes he spoke out loud to himself while he was driving

the vegetable lorry. 'What for?' Again and again: 'What for?' She was not a modern woman who cut her hair and wore short skirts. He had married a good plain Moslem woman who bore children and stamped her own chillies. He had a sudden vision of her at the duplicating machine, that night just before she was taken away, and he felt himself maddened, baffled and hopeless. He had become the ghost of a victim, hanging about the scene of a crime whose motive he could not understand and had not had time to learn.

The hunger strike at the prison went into the second week. Alone in the rattling cab of his lorry, he said things that he heard as if spoken by someone else, and his heart burned in fierce agreement with them. 'For a crowd of natives who'll smash our shops and kill us in our houses when their time comes.' 'She will starve herself to death there.' 'She will die there.' 'Devils who will burn and kill us.' He fell into bed each night like a stone, and dragged himself up in the mornings as a beast of burden is beaten to its feet.

One of these mornings, Girlie appeared very early, while he was wolfing bread and strong tea — alternate sensations of dry solidity and stinging heat — at the kitchen table. Her real name was Fatima, of course, but she had adopted the silly modern name along with the clothes of the young factory girls among whom she worked. She was expecting her first baby in a week or two, and her small face, her cut and curled hair and the sooty arches drawn over her eyebrows did not seem to belong to her thrust-out body under a clean smock. She wore mauve lipstick and was smiling her cocky little white girl's smile, foolish and bold, not like an Indian girl's at all.

'What's the matter?' he said.

She smiled again. 'Don't you know? I told Bobby he must get me up in time this morning. I wanted to be sure I wouldn't miss you today.'

'I don't know what you're talking about.'

She came over and put her arm up around his unwilling neck and kissed the grey bristles at the side of his mouth. 'Many happy returns! Don't you know it's your birthday?'

'No,' he said. 'I didn't know, didn't think —' He broke the pause by swiftly picking up the bread and giving his attention desperately to eating and drinking. His mouth was busy, but his eyes looked at her, intensely black. She said nothing, but stood there with him. She would not speak, and at last he said, swallowing a piece of bread that tore at his throat as it went down, 'I don't remember these things.'

The girl nodded, the Woolworth baubles in her ears swinging. 'That's the first thing she told me when I saw her yesterday – don't forget it's Bajie's birthday tomorrow.'

He shrugged over it. 'It means a lot to children. But that's how she is. Whether it's one of the old cousins or the neighbour's grandmother, she always knows when the birthday is. What importance is my birthday, while she's sitting there in a prison? I don't understand how she can do the things she does when her mind is always full of woman's nonsense at the same time – that's what I don't understand with her.'

'Oh, but don't you see?' the girl said. 'It's because she doesn't want anybody to be left out. It's because she always remembers; remembers everything – people without somewhere to live, hungry kids, boys who can't get educated – remembers all the time. That's how Ma is.'

'Nobody else is like that.' It was half a complaint.

'No, nobody else,' said his stepdaughter.

She sat herself down at the table, resting her belly. He put his head in his hands. 'I'm getting old' – but he was overcome by something much more curious, by an answer. He knew why he had desired her, the ugly widow with five children; he knew what way it was in which she was not like the others; it was there, like the fact of the belly that lay between him and her daughter.

Nadine Gordimer was born near Johannesburg in 1923. As a South African novelist and short story writer she had been outspoken in her stance against censorship and apartheid. Most of her work deals with the dilemmas of conscience involved in the race issue and the complexities of life under apartheid.

Collections of her short stories include: *The Soft Voice of the Serpent, Livingstones Companions, Not for Publication* (1976) and *Six Feet of the Country* (1982). Among her novels are *A World of Strangers* (1958), *Occasion for Loving* (1963), *Burger's Daughter* (1979) and *July's People* (1965).

Stench of Kerosene
■ *by Amrita Pritam* ■

Outside, a mare neighed. Guleri recognised the neighing and ran out of the house. The mare was from her parents' village. She put her head against its neck as if it were the door to her father's house.

Guleri's parents lived in Chamba. A few miles from her husband's village which was on high ground, the road curved and descended steeply downhill. From this point one could see Chamba lying a long way away at one's feet. Whenever Guleri was homesick she would take her husband, Manak, and go up to this point. She would see the homes of Chamba twinkling in the sunlight and would come back, her heart glowing with pride.

Once every year, after the harvest had been gathered in, Guleri was allowed to spend a few days with her parents. They sent a man to Lakarmandi to bring her back to Chamba. Two of her friends, who were also married to boys who lived away from Chamba, came home at the same time and the girls looked forward to their annual reunion, talking about their joys and sorrow. They went about the streets together. Then there was the harvest festival when the girls would have new clothes made for the occasion. Their *dupattas* would be dyed, starched and sprinkled with mica to make them glisten. They would buy glass bangles and silver ear-rings.

Guleri always counted the days to the harvest. When autumn breezes cleared the skies of monsoon clouds, she thought of little else. She went about her daily chores – fed the cattle, cooked food for her parents-in-law – and then sat back to work out how long it would be before someone came to fetch her from her parent's village.

And now, once again, it was time for her annual visit. She caressed the mare joyfully, greeted her father's servant, Natu, and made preparations to leave the next day. She did not have to express her excitement in words: the look on her face was enough. Her husband pulled at his *hookah* and closed his eyes. It seemed as if he either did not like the tobacco or that he could not bear to face his wife.

'You'll come to the fair at Chamba, won't you? Come even for a day,' she pleaded.

Manak put aside his *chillum* but did not reply. 'Why don't you answer me?' she asked, a little cross. 'Shall I tell you something?'

'I know what you're going to say – that you only go to your parents once a year. Well you've never been stopped before.'

'Then why do you want to stop me this time?' she demanded.

'Just this once,' he pleaded.

'Your mother's said nothing so why do you stand in the way?' Guleri was childishly stubborn.

'My mother . . .' Manak did not finish his sentence.

On the long-awaited morning, Guleri was ready long before dawn. She had no children and therefore no problem of having to leave them behind or take them with her. Natu saddled the mare as she took leave of Manak's parents. They patted her head and blessed her.

'I'll come with you for part of the way,' Manak said.

Guleri was happy as they set out. She hid Manak's flute under her *dupatta*.

After the village of Khajiar, the road descended steeply to Chamba. There she took out the flute and gave it to him. She took his hand in hers and said, 'Come now, play your flute.' But Manak, lost in his thoughts, paid no heed. 'Why don't you play your flute?' she asked, coaxing him. He looked at her sadly. Then putting the flute to his lips, blew a strange anguished wail.

'Guleri, don't go away,' he begged her. 'I ask again, don't go away this time.' He handed the flute to her, unable to continue.

'But why?' she asked. 'Come over on the day of the fair and we'll return together, I promise you.'

Manak did not ask again.

They stopped by the roadside. Natu took the mare a few paces ahead to leave the couple alone. It crossed Manak's mind that it was at this time of the year, seven years ago, that he and his friends had come on this very road to go to the harvest festival in Chamba. And it was at this fair that Manak had first seen Guleri and they had bartered their hearts to each other. Later, managing to meet her alone, he remembered taking her hand and telling her, 'You are like unripe corn – full of milk.'

'Cattle go for unripe corn,' Guleri had replied, freeing her hand with a jerk. 'Human beings prefer it roasted. If you want me, go and ask my father for my hand.'

Among Manak's kinsmen it was customary to settle the bride price before the wedding. Manak was nervous because he did not know the price Guleri's father would demand from him. But Guleri's father was prosperous and had lived in cities. He had sworn that he would not take money for his daughter but would give her to a worthy young man from a good family. Manak, he decided, answered these requirements and soon after, Guleri and Manak were married. Deep in memories, Manak was roused by Guleri's hand on his shoulder.

'What are you dreaming of?' she teased him.

He did not answer. The mare neighed impatiently and Guleri got up to leave. 'Do you know the bluebell wood a couple of miles from here?' she asked. 'It's said that anyone who goes through it becomes deaf. You must have passed through that bluebell wood. You don't seem to be hearing anything I say.'

'You're right, Guleri. I can't hear anything you're saying to me,' and Manak sighed.

They looked at each other. Neither understood the other's thoughts. 'I'll go now,' Guleri said gently. 'You'd better go back. You've come a long way from home.'

'You've walked all the distance. You'd better get on the mare,' replied Manak.

'Here, take your flute.'

'You take it.'

'Will you come and play it on the day of the fair?' she asked with a smile. The sun shone in her eyes. Manak turned his face away. Perplexed, Guleri shrugged her shoulders and took the road to Chamba. Manak returned home.

He entered the house and slumped listlessly on the *charpoy*. 'You've been away a long time,' exclaimed his mother. 'Did you go all the way to Chamba?'

'Not all the way, only to the top of the hill.' Manak's voice was heavy.

'Why do you croak like an old woman?' said his mother severely. 'Be a man.'

Manak wanted to retort, 'You are a woman; why don't you cry like one for a change!' But he remained silent.

Manak and Guleri had been married seven years but she had never borne a child and Manak's mother had made a secret resolve that she would not let it go beyond the eighth year. This year, true to her decision, she had paid five hundred *rupees* to get him a second wife and she was waiting, as Manak knew, for Guleri to go to her parents before bringing in the new bride. Obedient to his mother and to custom, Manak's body responded to the new woman but his heart was dead within him.

In the early hours one morning he was smoking his chillum when an old friend happened to pass by. 'Ho, Bhavani, where are you going so early in the morning?'

Bhavani stopped. He had a small bundle on his shoulder. 'Nowhere in particular,' he said evasively.

'You should be on your way to some place or the other,' exclaimed Manak. 'What about a smoke?'

Bhavani sat down on his haunches and took the chillum from

24

Manak's hands. 'I'm going to Chamba for the fair,' he said at last.

Bhavani's words pierced through Manak's heart like a needle. 'Is the fair today?'

'It's the same day, every year,' replied Bhavani drily. 'Don't you remember, we were in the same party seven years ago?' Bhavani did not say any more but Manak was conscious of the other man's rebuke and he felt uneasy. Bhavani put down the chillum and picked up his bundle. His flute was sticking out of the bundle. Manak's eye remained on the flute till Bhavani disappeared from view.

Next morning, Manak was in his fields when he saw Bhavani coming back but he looked the other way deliberately. He did not want to talk to Bhavani to hear anything about the fair. But Bhavani came round the other side and sat down in front of Manak. His face was sad and grey as a cinder.

'Guleri is dead,' Bhavani said in a flat voice.

'What?'

'When she heard of your second marriage, she soaked her clothes in kerosene and set fire to them.'

Manak, mute with pain, could only stare and feel his own life burning out.

The days went by. Manak resumed his work in the fields and ate his meals when they were given to him. But he was like a dead man, his face blank, his eyes empty.

'I am not his wife,' complained his second wife. 'I'm just someone he happened to marry.'

But quite soon she was pregnant and Manak's mother was pleased with her new daughter-in-law. She told Manak about his wife's condition, but he looked as if he did not understand and his eyes were still empty.

His mother encouraged her daughter-in-law to bear with her husband's moods for a few days. As soon as the child was born and placed in his father's lap, she said, Manak would change.

A son was duly born to Manak's wife; and his mother, rejoicing, bathed the boy, dressed him in fine clothes and put him in Manak's lap. Manak stared at the new-born babe in his lap. He stared a long time, uncomprehending, his face as usual expressionless. Then suddenly the blank eyes filled with horror and Manak began to scream. 'Take him away!' he shrieked hysterically, 'Take him away! He stinks of kerosene.'

Amrita Pritam was born in 1919 in the Punjab. Her stories have been translated from the original Punjabi by Kushwat Singh. She is best known on the sub-continent of India as a poet and her prose style reflects her love of poetry. Her most celebrated work is an elegy in ballad form on the partition of India. In her short stories she writes about love in all its many aspects, dealing equally well with high caste, well-educated women as with more humble villagers. Her work includes the novellas *Skeleton* (1973) and *Line in Water* (1975).

Snowdrops

■ *by Leslie Norris* ■

Today Miss Webster was going to show them the snowdrops growing in the little three-cornered garden outside the school-keeper's house, where they weren't allowed to go. All through the winter, Miss Webster said, the snowdrops had been asleep under the ground, but now they were up, growing in the garden. He tried to think what they would look like, but all he could imagine was one flake of the falling snow, bitterly frail and white, and nothing like a flower.

It was a very cold morning. He leaned against the kitchen table, feeling the hard edge against his chest, eating his breakfast slowly. His brother, Geraint, who was only three, sat in an armchair close to the fire. He could see the shape of Geraint's head outlined against the flames and he saw with wonder that the fire had given to his brother's legs a glow of red only slightly less bright than the leaping flames. Geraint was eating a bowl of porridge, and what he did was this. He would make a crater in the porridge with his spoon, and then he'd watch the milk run in and fill the hole up. Then he would dip his spoon in the milk and drink it. The boy watched his brother.

'Hurry up,' said the boy's mother, 'or you'll never get to school!'

'Miss Webster is going to show us the snowdrops today,' he said.

'That's nice,' said his mother, looking out of the window at the grey morning. 'I wonder where your father is.'

His father came in and filled the room with bigness. He stood in front of the fire, because it was cold in the yard, and all the boy could see was a faint light each side of his father's wide body.

'It's a cold wind,' said his father. 'I can't remember a colder March.'

The man turned around and faced them, smiling because he was much warmer and the cold March wind was safely locked outside the house.

'You're a big boy for six,' he said to the boy, 'and it's all because you eat your breakfast up.'

This was a joke his father always said, and the boy smiled, thinking all the time of the snowdrops. Would it be too cold to go and see them? Perhaps Miss Webster would take only the boys, he comforted himself, because they were stronger, and the girls could stay in school out of the cold.

'The Meredith boy is being buried this afternoon,' his father was saying to his mother. 'I'm sorry I shan't be able to go. I worked with his father for two and a half years, up at the rolling mill. A nice man, Charlie Meredith, very quiet. I hear he's very cut up, and his wife too. This was their only boy.'

'How old was he?' asked his mother.

'Twenty,' his father said. 'Twenty last January. Silly little fool. That bike was too powerful for him – well, to go at that speed on a wet, dark night. Over seventy, the police said, straight into the back of a stationary truck. A terrible mess.'

'He was a nice-looking boy, too,' said his mother.

'All the Merediths are,' said his father. 'This one was very friendly with the young teacher up at the school, Webber, is it? Something like that.'

But his mother coughed and looked sharply at the boy.

'Oh?' said his father. 'Of course. I should have remembered. Come on, son, or you'll be late.'

It seemed much warmer when he got to school and he took off his overcoat next to Edmund Jenkins. Edmund had a long blue scarf which his big sister had knitted for him. They each held an end of the scarf and raced up the corridor, seeing how many children they could catch, but Miss Lewis stopped them. Then Edmund told him a joke.

'What's the biggest rope in the world?' Edmund asked.

The boy didn't know.

'Europe,' said Edmund, and they both laughed.

They were still laughing as they went into the classroom, although Miss Webster wasn't there. After a time Miss Lewis came in and sent the children into other classrooms. Miss Lewis took the top class and she was very stern and strict. He and Edmund had to go to Miss Lewis's class.

'Europe,' said Edmund Jenkins to him, very quietly, as they went into the top class. Edmund was very brave.

It wasn't too bad in Miss Lewis's class, because they had some interesting books there and the arithmetic was not difficult. When you looked out of the window, too, you saw a different part of the playground. The boy could almost see a corner of the school-keeper's house, so he wasn't very far away from the snowdrops.

Just before playtime Miss Lewis told all the children from Miss Webster's class that they could go back to their own room after play. The boy grinned in delight. Everything would be all right, he told himself. After play they would surely go to see the flowers.

Out in the playground they all began to run about, except Gerald Davis, who seemed to fall over whatever he did. He was quite unable to make even the tiniest step without tumbling down, and his face was red from laughing and because he didn't know what was happening to him. Edmund Jenkins was standing close by and the boy could see that Edmund had been up to his tricks again.

'What's happening to Gerald?' he asked.

But Edmund only pointed to Gerald's boots, and then the boy saw that his laces had been tied together, the left boot to the right boot and the right boot to the left boot, so that Gerald was hobbled. Some boys were beginning to imitate Gerald, falling about although their boots weren't tied together. After a while he and Edmund untied the laces and Gerald went whooping up the gravel yard like a released pigeon.

He walked with Edmund towards the last corner of the playground, away from the wind, and they took their small packets of sandwiches from their pockets. Edmund had three sandwiches, with marmalade in them, and he had two sandwiches, but he didn't know what they were filled with. He bit one of them to find out.

The taste was incredibly new and marvellous, filling the whole of his mouth with delight and pleasure. He shook his head to show Edmund how wonderful the taste was, and then let Edmund have a bite.

'What's in it, Edmund?' he asked. 'What's in my sandwich?'

'Bacon,' said Edmund. 'It's only bacon.'

The boy was incredulous. He opened the second sandwich to inspect the filling. It didn't look like bacon.

'It can't be,' he said. 'I have bacon for my breakfast every morning. I had some *this* morning.'

'I know,' said Edmund 'but it tastes different when it's cold.'

Together they walked as far as the shed in which the coal was stored. This was as far as they were allowed to go. Not very far away, but tantalisingly around the corner and down the little path that led to the garden, the snowdrops were growing.

'Do you wish,' said the boy, 'that Miss Webster will take us to see the flowers when play is over?'

'I don't care,' said Edmund, 'because I've seen some already, growing in my aunt's garden.'

The boy looked at his best friend, deciding carefully whether he would ask him to describe a snowdrop. But he would wait, he thought, to see them for himself, and then the bell was ringing to call them in.

The children cheered and clapped when they saw Miss Webster. She was dressed in a black frock, without any jewellery, but she smiled at them, holding her finger to her lips for them to be quiet.

The bandage she had on one finger, where she had trapped it in the cupboard door and hadn't cried, looked very white and clean. She gave them some crayons and a big sheet of paper for each child and they could draw whatever they liked.

The boy drew a robin. He hadn't drawn a robin since Christmas but just recently he had been watching one that came to his garden every day, and now he knew just how the bird's head fitted on to its round little body, and he had seen the way the legs, as thin as pieces of wire, splayed out underneath. Sometimes the robin looked like a hunchback, but he would draw this robin standing up bravely, throwing out his red chest before he sang. And the robin's song was odd. It wasn't very long, and it dropped and fell like threads of falling water. The boy closed his eyes a little while so that he could hear the robin, but he couldn't get it quite right. Soon he was engrossed in watching his robin grow on the paper. With infinite care he set its delicate feet on a brown twig, not just a flat stick as he had drawn at Christmas, but a real twig, with little knobs on it where the buds would be. At last it was finished and he leaned back in his chair, looking around as he did so. Nearly all the other children had completed their drawings some time before and they were reading their books. Miss Webster was sitting at her desk, her head in her hands. Everything was very still. The boy took out his book and began to read, but most of the time he looked at the robin he had drawn.

This is what he was doing when the bell ended morning school and they were dismissed for home. Miss Webster looked at his robin and she liked it. She took it from his desk and pinned it in a good place on the wall, where everybody could see it. The boy was pleased and surprised, because he had never before had a drawing pinned up in this way, although he knew he could draw at least as well as Edmund, who had a drawing selected nearly every week.

'Shall we be going to see the snowdrops this afternoon?' he asked Miss Webster before he went home.

'Yes,' she said, 'if Miss Lewis will allow us, we'll go to see them this afternoon.'

He ate his lunch quietly, thinking in his head of a story about a wizard who could change himself into anything at all. It was a good story, but something always seemed to happen before he got to the end of it. Sometimes he began it at night in bed, only to fall asleep long before the really exciting part. Now his mother was talking to him.

'Was Miss Webster in school this morning?' she asked. His

31

mother was knitting a pullover. The needles went over and under each other with the same little slide and click, and a row of knitting grew magically behind them.

'Yes,' he said, 'but she came late. She didn't arrive until playtime.'

'Poor girl,' said his mother.

He thought about this for a long time.

'She's got a bad hand,' he said. 'She caught her finger in the cupboard door and her hand was bleeding. She's got a bandage on it today. She'll never be able to bend her finger again, that's what Edmund Jenkins said.'

'Oh, you and Edmund Jenkins,' said his mother.

He raced back to school, his boots ringing on the pavement as they always seemed to in cold weather. Every day he went a special way, over the river bridge, being very careful of the traffic, up Penry Street as far as the fruiterer's, then across the road by the fire station in case the doors were open; now he could balance along a low wall outside Jack William's garden, and at last he was in the small road where the school was. He never knew what would happen here, because he would meet many boys going to school and almost any adventure could happen. Once in this road Bernard Spencer had given him a glass marble, and once he and Edmund had found a silver medal which somebody had won for running. Edmund's father had taken it to the police, but they didn't have a reward.

But there was nobody about, except some girls skipping and giggling just inside the school yard, and he made his way inside the building. Everybody was sitting very quietly inside the classroom. They were allowed to go in early because it was very cold. Normally they would have stayed outside until Miss Lewis rang the bell, and some boys stayed outside however wet and cold it was, but today it seemed that they all wanted to sit quietly with Miss Webster, close to the cast-iron stove that had the figure of a tortoise on the top.

At two o'clock Miss Webster marked her register and then began to tell them a story. It was a good story, about a dragon who guarded a hoard of treasure in his den underground, where the snowdrops slept all through the winter. From time to time Miss Webster turned her head to look at the big clock in the hall. She could see it through the top half of the classroom door, which had four panes of glass in it. Her voice seemed to be hoarser than usual, which was fine when she read the dragon's bits, but not

32

good for the knight nor the princess. She shut her book with a snap and stood up. She hadn't completed the story.

'Now we'll go to see the snowdrops,' she said. 'I want the girls to go quietly to the cloakroom and put on their coats. When they are ready, I'll come along with the boys. Everybody must wear a coat. If you have difficulty with buttons, please stand in front and I'll fasten them for you.'

He stood up with a sudden lightening of the heart. He had known all the time that Miss Webster would not forget, and at last she was taking him to see the miraculous flowers, pale and fragile as the falling snow. He looked at Miss Webster with gratitude. Her eyes were bright as frost, and she was making sure that the girls walked nicely through the door. Edmund Jenkins waved at him and that was funny, because Edmund had his black gloves on with a hole in a place he could push his finger through. Edmund waved his finger like a fat white worm in the middle of his dark hand.

They all walked beautifully through the playground, in two rows holding hands, and he held Edmund's hand and they gave a little skip together every three steps. It didn't take long to get to the garden. The children bent down, four at a time, to look at the little clump of snowdrops and Miss Webster told them what to look at. He and Edmund would be last to look. When they had finished, the other children went down to the garden gate which opened onto the road. It was a big gate with iron bars and your head could almost poke through. Somewhere a long way off the boy could hear men singing. They sang softly, mournfully, the words carried gently on the air over the school wall, but the boy could not hear what they said.

'It's a funeral,' said Edmund. 'My father's there and my Uncle Jim. It's a boy who was killed on a motor-bike.'

The boy nodded. Funerals often passed the school on their way to the cemetery at the top of the valley. All the men wore black suits and they walked slowly. Sometimes they sang.

He squatted down to look at the snowdrops. He felt a slow, sad disappointment. He looked around for Miss Webster to explain these simple flowers to him, but she had gone down to the gate and was staring through, looking up the road. Her back was as hard as a stone. He turned again to the snowdrops, concentrating, willing them to turn marvellous in front of his eyes. They hung down their four petalled heads in front of him, the white tinged with minute green, the little green ball sturdily holding the petals, the greyish leaves standing up like miniature spears. The boy began to see their fragility. He saw them blow in a sudden gust of the cold March wind, shake, and straighten gallantly. He imagined them standing all night in the dark garden, holding bravely to their specks of whiteness. He put out a finger to touch the nearest flower, knowing now what snowdrops were. He lifted his face to tell Miss Webster, but she was standing right at the gate, holding the iron bars with her hands. Her shoulders were shaking.

> *Mor ddedwydd yw y rhai trwy ffydd*
> *S'yn mynd o blith y byw* ...

sang the men as they filed solemnly past the school. The boy knew it was Welsh because of his grandmother, and it was sad and beautiful.

After a while they couldn't hear the singing any more, but Miss Webster continued to cry aloud in the midst of the frightened children.

* So blessed are the ones through faith
That go about the living ...

Leslie Norris is a Welsh poet and story-writer, who now lives in Chichester. Many of his stories collected in *Sliding* (1978) were originally written for American magazines like the *New Yorker*. They reflect his interest in country matters and life in small communities. He has been described as capturing 'the quick terrors of boyhood, the unpleasant surprises of middle-age and the pace of lives falling into inconsequence' (Dent edition, 1978). His poems are collected in *Mountains, Polecats, Pheasants and Other Elegies* (Chatto and Windus, 1974).

The Fly-paper

■ by Elizabeth Taylor ■

On Wednesdays, after school, Sylvia took the bus to the outskirts of the nearest town for her music lesson. Because of her docile manner, she did not complain of the misery she suffered in Miss Harrison's darkened parlour, sitting at the old-fashioned upright piano with its brass candlesticks and loose, yellowed keys. In the highest register there was not the faintest tinkle of a note, only the hollow sound of the key being banged down. Although that distant octave was out of her range, Sylvia sometimes pressed down one of its notes, listening mutely to Miss Harrison's exasperated railings about her – Sylvia's – lack of aptitude, or even concentration. The room was darkened in winter by a large fir-tree pressing against – in windy weather tapping against – the window, and in summer even more so by holland blinds, half-drawn to preserve the threadbare carpet. To add to all the other miseries, Sylvia had to peer short-sightedly at the music-book, her glance going up and down between it and the keyboard, losing her place, looking hunted, her lips pursed.

It was now the season of the drawn blinds, and she waited in the lane at the bus-stop, feeling hot in her winter coat, which her grandmother insisted on her wearing, just as she insisted on the music lessons. The lane buzzed in the heat of the late afternoon – with bees in the clover, and flies going crazy over some cow-pats on the road.

Since her mother's death, Sylvia had grown glum and sullen. She was a plain child, plump, mature for her eleven years. Her greasy hair was fastened back by a pink plastic slide; her tweed coat, of which, last winter, she had been rather proud, had cuffs and collar of mock ocelot. She carried, beside her music case, a shabby handbag, once her mother's.

The bus seemed to tremble and jingle as it came slowly down the road. She climbed on, and sat down on the long seat inside the door, where a little air might reach her.

On the other long seat opposite her, was a very tall man; quite old, she supposed, for his hair was carefully arranged over his bald skull. He stared at her. She puffed with the heat and then, to avoid his glance, she slewed round a little to look over her shoulder at the dusty hedges – the leaves all in late summer darkness. She was sure that he was wondering why she wore a winter's coat on such a day, and she unbuttoned it and flapped it a little to air her armpits. The weather had a threat of change in it, her grandmother had said, and her cotton dress was too short. It had already been let down and had a false hem, which she now tried to draw down over her thighs.

'Yes, it is very warm,' the man opposite her suddenly said, as if agreeing with someone else's remark.

She turned in surprise, and her face reddened, but she said nothing.

After a while, she began to wonder if it would be worth getting off at the fare-stage before the end of her journey and walk the rest of the way. Then she could spend the money on a lolly. She had to waste half-an-hour before her lesson, and must wander about somewhere to pass the time. It would be better to be wandering about with a lolly to suck. Her grandmother did not allow her to eat sweets – bathing the teeth in acid, she said it was.

'I believe I have seen you before,' the man opposite said, 'Either wending your way to or from a music-lesson, I imagine.' He looked knowingly at her music-case.

'To,' she said sullenly.

'A budding Myra Hess,' he went on. 'I take it that you play the piano, as you seem to have no instrument secreted about your person.'

She did not know what he meant, and stared out the window, frowning, feeling so hot and anguished.

'And what is your name?' he asked. 'We shall have to keep it in mind for the future when you are famous.'

'Sylvia Wilkinson,' she said under her breath.

'Not bad. Not bad. Sylvia. No doubt one day I shall boast that I met the great Sylvia Wilkinson on a bus one summer's afternoon. Name-dropping, you know. A harmless foible of the humble.'

He was very neat and natty, but his reedy voice had a nervous tremour. All this time, he had held an unlighted cigarette in his hand, and gestured with it, but made no attempt to find matches.

'I expect at school you sing the beautiful song, 'Who is Sylvia?' Do you?'

She shook her head, without looking at him and, to her horror, he began to sing quaveringly, 'Who is Sylvia? What is she-he?'

A woman sitting a little further down the bus, turned and looked at him sharply.

He's mad, Sylvia decided. She was embarrassed, but not nervous, not nervous at all, here in the bus with other people, in spite of all her grandmother had said about not getting into conversations with strangers.

He went on singing, wagging his cigarette in time.

The woman turned again and gave him a longer stare. She was homely-looking, Sylvia decided – in spite of fair hair going very

37

dark at the roots. She had a comfortable, protective manner, as if she were keeping an eye on the situation for Sylvia's sake.

Suddenly, he broke off his singing and returned her stare. 'I take it, Madam,' he said, 'that you do not appreciate my singing.'

'I should think it's hardly the place,' she said shortly. 'That's all,' and turned her head away.

'Hardly the place!' he said, in a low voice, as if to himself, and with feigned amazement. 'On a fair summer's afternoon, while we bowl merrily along the lanes. Hardly the place – to express one's joy of living! I am sorry,' he said to Sylvia, in a louder voice. 'I had not realised we were going to a funeral.'

Thankfully, she saw that they were coming nearer to the outskirts of the town. It was not a large town, and its outskirts were quiet.

'I hope you don't mind me chatting to you,' the man said to Sylvia. 'I am fond of children. I am known as being *good* with them. Well known for that. I treat them on my own level, as one should.'

Sylvia stared – almost glared – out of the window, twisted round in her seat, her head aching with the stillness of her eyes.

It was flat country, intersected by canals. On the skyline, were the clustered chimneys of a brick-works. The only movement out there was the faintest shimmering of heat.

She was filled by misery; for there seemed nothing in her life now but acquiescence to hated things, and her grandmother's old ways setting her apart from other children. Nothing she did was what she wanted to do – school-going, church-going, now this terrible music lesson ahead of her. Since her mother's death, her life had taken a sharp turn for the worse, and she could not see how it would ever be any better. She had no faith in freeing herself from it, even when she was grown-up.

A wasp zigzagged across her and settled on the front of her coat. She was obliged to turn. She sat rigid, her head held back, her chin tucked in, afraid to make a movement.

'Allow me!' The awful man opposite had reached across the bus, and flapped a crumpled handkerchief at her. The wasp began to fuss furiously, darting about her face.

'We'll soon settle you, you little pest,' the man said, making matters worse.

The bus-conductor came between them. He stood carefully still for a moment, and then decisively clapped his hands together, and the wasp fell dead to the ground.

'Thank you,' Sylvia said to him, but not to the other.

They were passing bungalows now, newly-built, and with unmade gardens. Looking directly ahead of her, Sylvia got up, and went to the platform of the bus, standing there in a slight breeze, ready for the stopping-place.

Beyond the bus-shelter, she knew that there was a little general shop. She would comfort herself with a bright red lolly on a stick. She crossed the road and stood looking in the window, at jars of boiled sweets, and packets of detergents and breakfast cereals. There was a notice about ice-creams, but she had not enough money.

She turned to go into the empty, silent shop when the now familiar and dreaded voice came from beside her. 'Would you care to partake of an ice, this hot afternoon?'

He stood between her and the shop, and the embarrassment she had suffered on the bus gave way to terror.

'An ice?' he repeated, holding his head on one side, looking at her imploringly.

She thought that if she said 'yes', she could at least get inside the shop. Someone must be there to serve, someone whose protection she might depend upon. Those words of warning from her grandmother came into her head, cautionary tales, dark with unpleasant hints.

Before she could move, or reply, she felt a hand lightly but firmly touch her shoulder. It was the glaring woman from the bus, she was relieved to see.

'Haven't you ever been told not to talk to strangers?' she asked Sylvia, quite sharply, but with calm common sense in her brusqueness. '*You'd* better be careful,' she said to the man menacingly. 'Now come along, child, and let this be a lesson to you. Which way were you going?'

Sylvia nodded ahead.

'Well, best foot forward, and keep going. And *you*, my man, can kindly step in a different direction, or I'll find a policeman.'

At this last word, Sylvia turned to go, feeling flustered, but important.

'You should *never*,' the woman began, going along beside her. 'There's some funny people about these days. Doesn't your mother warn you?'

'She's dead.'

'Oh, well, I'm sorry about that. My God, it's warm.' She pulled her dress away from her bosom, fanning it. She had a shopping-basket full of comforting, homely groceries, and Sylvia looked into it, as she walked beside her.

'Wednesday's always my day,' the woman said. 'Early-closing here, so I take the bus up to Horseley. I have a relative who has the little general store there. It makes a change, but not in this heat.'

She rambled on about her uninteresting affairs. Once, Sylvia glanced back, and could see the man still standing there, gazing after them.

'I shouldn't turn round,' the woman said. 'Which road did you say?'

Sylvia hadn't, but now did so.

'Well, you can come my way. That would be better, and there's nothing much in it. Along by the gravel-pits. I'll have a quick look round before we turn the corner.'

When she did so, she said that she thought they were being followed, at a distance. 'Oh, it's disgraceful,' she said. 'And with all the things you read in the papers. You can't be too careful, and you'll have to remember that in the future. I'm not sure I ought not to inform the police.'

Along this road, there were disused gravel-pits, and chicory and convolvulus. Rusty sorrel and rustier tin-cans gave the place a derelict air. On the other side, there were allotments, and ramshackle tool-sheds among dark nettles.

'It runs into Hamilton Road,' the woman explained.

'But I don't have to be there for another half-hour,' Sylvia said nervously. She could imagine Miss Harrison's face if she turned up on the doorstep all that much too soon, in the middle of a lesson with the bright-looking girl she had often met leaving.

'I'm going to give you a nice cup of tea, and make sure you're all right. Don't you worry.'

Thankfully, she turned in at the gate of a little red brick house at the edge of the waste land. It was ugly, but very neat, and surrounded by hollyhocks. The beautifully shining windows were draped with frilly, looped-up curtains, with plastic flowers arranged between them.

Sylvia followed the woman down a side path to the back door, trying to push her worries from her mind. She was all right this time, but what of all the future Wednesdays, she wondered – with their perilous journeys to be made alone.

She stood in the kitchen and looked about her. It was clean and cool there. A budgerigar hopped in a cage. Rather listlessly, but not knowing what else to do, she went to it and ran her finger-nail along the wires.

'There's my baby boy, my little Joey,' the woman said in a sing-song, automatic way, as she held the kettle under the tap. 'You'll feel better when you've had a cup of tea,' she added, now supposedly addressing Sylvia.

'It's very kind of you.'

'Any woman would do the same. There's a packet of Oval Marie in my basket, if you'd like to open it and put them on this plate.'

Sylvia was glad to do something. She arranged the biscuits carefully on the rose-patterned plate. 'It's very nice here,' she said. Her grandmother's house was so dark and cluttered; Miss Harrison's even more so. Both smelt stuffy, of thick curtains and old furniture. She did not go into many houses, for she was so seldom invited anywhere. She was a dull girl, whom nobody liked very much, and she knew it.

'I must have everything sweet and fresh,' the woman said complacently.

The kettle began to sing.

I've still got to get home, Sylvia thought in a panic. She stared up at a fly-paper hanging in the window – the only disconcerting thing in the room. Some of the flies were still half alive, and striving hopelessly to free themselves. But they were caught forever.

She heard footsteps on the path, and listened in surprise; but the woman did not seem to hear, or lift her head. She was spooning tea from the caddy into the teapot.

'Just in time, Herbert,' she called out.

Sylvia turned round as the door opened. With astonished horror, she saw the man from the bus step confidently into the kitchen.

'Well done, Mabel!' he said, closing the door behind him. 'Don't forget one for the pot!' He smiled, smoothing his hands together, surveying the room.

Sylvia spun round questioningly to the woman, who was now bringing the teapot to the table, and she noticed for the first time that there were three cups and saucers laid there.

'Well, sit down, do,' the woman said, a little impatiently. 'It's all ready.'

Elizabeth Taylor was born in Reading in 1912 and died in 1975 in Penn, Buckinghamshire, where she spent most of her married life. She worked first as a governess and later as a librarian. Her first novel, *At Mrs Lippincotes* (1945), was written during the Second World War, while her husband fought in the RAF. She has published several collections of short stories including, *Hester Lilly and Other Stories* (1958), *The Blush and Other Stories*, *A Dedicated Man and Other Stories* (1958) *The Devastating Boys (1972).*

Jane is a Girl

■ *by Walter Macken* ■

He hastily gulped the tea remaining in his cup, grabbed the piece of bread and jam from his plate, started to stuff it into his mouth as he rose from the chair and was stopped by his mother's voice: 'Sit down! Where are you going?' and as he went to answer: 'Don't talk with your mouth full!'

Jude thought she was most unreasonable.

'Now?' she queried, when she saw he had swallowed the bite.

'Out,' he said.

'Mother,' she said automatically.

'Mother,' he said.

'Be in here at eight o'clock,' she said. 'Not a minute after. Don't have me chasing you or you'll feel the weight of my hand.'

'All right,' he said, moving.

'Mother,' she said.

'Mother,' he said.

'Will I ever put manners into you?' she asked the ceiling.

He was going the back way into the yard from the kitchen, when he stopped and thought. Then he turned and ran up the stairs. He went into a room there. His big brother was in front of the mirror brushing his hair.

'Give us a tanner, Joe,' he suggested.

'Get out of here,' said Joe. 'I want all my tanners.'

'Spending them on old girls,' said Jude.

He banged the door and ran. Joe didn't chase him. At the foot of the stairs he went into the other bedroom. His sister screamed. She was only half-dressed.

'How dare you come into a lady's room without knocking?' she shouted, hurriedly covering herself.

What a stupid fuss about nothing, Jude thought. 'Give us a tanner, Nora?' he asked.

'What do you want sixpence for?' she asked. 'Don't use slang.'

'Sweets,' he said.

'I can only give you tuppence,' she said. 'It's all I can afford.' She reached for her handbag.

'Oh, all right,' he said, holding out his hand.

'Go and wash that dirty hand,' she said, putting the pennies into it.

'All right,' he said. 'You smell nice.' He said this just to please her. He didn't like all the scents, but that wasn't too bad.

'Close the door after you,' Nora said.

He did so, and went to the sink in the yard and washed his hands with the big bar of white soap. He didn't want to go back

44

into the kitchen for the towel so he just went out the back way shaking his hands to dry them.

He went round the corner into the small market-place. There was a shop here. Jude looked into the window. He decided on bull's-eyes which were eight a penny. Each one, uncrunched, lasted for five to ten minutes. That meant nearly two hours of minty sweetness if you gave away only four at the most.

Jude took one from the bag and put it under his tongue. This was the best way to make it last. He went back to his street. It seemed empty, houses on one side facing houses on the other side, their front doors opening on to the pavements. The people were hidden by lace curtains and geraniums in pots. It was a Sunday evening in March.

Jude hoisted himself on the wide window-sill of one of the houses. He knew this was a house where they didn't mind you sitting on the window-sill. Others did. They would roar at you, frightening the life out of you if you weren't anticipating it.

He now shifted the sweet from under his tongue to his cheek and made it bulge there. He knew this would attract custom because, although there didn't seem to be a living soul inhabiting those houses, there would be small eyes watching the street.

Sure enough four principals to use his sweets on. There were several games they could play. Marbles were not in season, so it would have to be rounders at the four corners where one street bisected the other. On the whole he decided they would play hurling. It was more exciting and would warm him up on a cold evening, so when Jane came out of the house, he took the bag of sweets out of his pocket and looked into it. That brought her. 'Have a sweet,' he said, handing her one. She took it, so he knew she was enrolled. Pat Fane, Jonjo and Tip Heaney were the other three, so they leaned against the wall, sucking carefully at their sweets. Some of the smaller children also arrived and sat on the kerb or stood with their hands behind their backs, looking, and their mouths watering. Jude knew this was slightly cruel, but how could he dish out sweets to all of them?

He got off the window-sill, crunched his sweet to bits and said: 'We will play hurling.' They considered this for a moment, and then they ran. He ran himself down the street, around the backs of the houses, into his own yard where he picked up the hurley stick and the soft rubber ball. When he got back to the street, the others were scurrying about. His own hurling stick was in good shape. The boss had been broken but he had repaired it with a band of tin that came wrapped around fruit boxes. Jane had a good hurley stick, too, better than his own. The others had make-shift hurleys, that were mostly bits of stick with a crude curve at the end, but they were well used and as precious to them as if they were due to play in an all-Ireland hurling final.

He picked his team. He took Tip Heaney who was the biggest of them and a bit rough, while Jane had Pat Fane and Jonjo. They divided the small ones up between them. The boys took off their coats and put them on the ground to act as goalposts. They sent two of the smallest to each end of the street to watch out for the police, because at this time some of the people took to talking in the Council about the way you couldn't walk the streets of the city without being belted with balls or knocked down with racing kids. Hadn't they homes to go to or the wide spaces of the municipal playing fields? All that stuff, so you had to post sentries.

Jane and himself put the ball in the middle of the street. Then they hit their hurleys on the ground, clashed them three times and then scrambled for the ball. The game was on. It was vigorous. It was interrupted once or twice when irate mothers ran out to take their children's best Sunday clothes from the dusty road, brushing them angrily, and shaking their fists before departing. They replaced the lost goalposts with rocks. Once the ball hit a window and all of them stood like statues waiting for the result, ready to run if the reaction was hostile. Nothing happened so they continued to play.

Jude's side was being defeated. The combination of Jane, Pat Fane and Jonjo was too powerful. Jude himself was fast and slick, but Tip was too slow and heavy, and even the little tricks he used like putting the hurley between his opponent's legs to trip him were unavailing in the end.

So they had to take to argument. It was a goal! It wasn't a goal! It went outside the stone. Didn't it? Yes it did! No it didn't! You stupid idiot, are you blind? The veins on their necks stood out as they tried to outshout one another.

This led to a lot of heat and a lot of vigour. It developed into a furious struggle between Jude and Jane. Each time the ball came to them, they slashed and heaved and threw their bodies at one another until one got the victory and belted the ball away. Sometimes Jane won those struggles and sometimes Jude, and they glared at one another like animals. Now! See! I told you! Jude had cuts on his knees and Jane's stockings were torn. They were egged on by the others. The street was a canon of shrill screams and shouts being deflected into the sky.

This last time the ball was in the air, and they were pressing together looking up, watching its descent. They raised their hurleys to catch it. It came down between them, the ball escaped and Jude fell on top of her.

Now as he fell, shouting, his forehead was practically touching hers. He could see her wide eyes and the bead of sweat between her eye-brows and her white teeth snarling at him from drawnback red lips. Something happened between them. He saw her face changing as she looked up at him, the excitement dying out of her eyes. He was conscious of feeling different inside himself. This game he had engineered no longer mattered. He was suddenly very conscious that the shape of her body was different from his own.

This is when it came into his mind. Why, Jane is a girl! Jane is a girl! He was suddenly embarrassed. His face was red from exertion before. Now it seemed to him to get redder. He got to his feet. She got up too. She avoided his eyes.

Jude couldn't stand this any longer. He turned and walked away from the field. They were stunned. They called after him: 'Hey, Jude! Where are you going? Hey, Jude!'

He was in an agony of embarrassment. He was upset. He wanted to run, but this would look bad. Instead he took the bag of sweets from his pocket, looked at it and threw it towards them. The bag burst and the sweets flew all over the place. They stopped calling then and scrambled for the sweets, laughing. Jane didn't. She had gone to the path and stood there with her back turned. Did she feel the same? he wondered. Did she say, why Jude is a boy?

He went in the back way to his house. He put his hands under the tap. He filled his palms and sloshed the cold water on his face. His face was hot. He washed the blood from his knee cuts so that his mother wouldn't be fighting about them. Then he went into the kitchen. There was nobody there. He sat on the wooden stool in front of the fire, rested his elbows on his knees, his chin on his hands, and he thought. Why should it be different? he wondered. What difference does it make? Now he could see that she had long hair, that she wore dresses, that she was good-looking, but she was a Girl. Wasn't she always one? What was the difference now? Now that he came to think of it Pat Fane was also a girl, and she had fair hair.

'Are you sick or something, Jude?' his mother asked. 'Sitting there gazing into the fire. Why aren't you out playing?' He thought he might tell her. But then he didn't. She was always very busy. She sat sewing and listening to the radio. There was a knock at the front door and she put down the sewing and went to answer it.

His sister came down to the kitchen now, ready to go out. She was all dolled up. She looked at the silent boy.

'What's wrong, Jude?' she asked.

'Jane is a girl,' said Jude, thinking she would understand.

'Say that again,' she said.

'Jane is a girl,' he said.

'Well, what did you think she was, a rhinoceros?' she asked.

'Hey, Joe, Joe!' she was calling. 'Come here while I tell you!'

'No, no!' pleaded Jude.

Joe came downstairs fixing his tie. Nora was laughing.

'Guess what?' she asked. 'Jude has discovered that Jane is a girl.'

'What, at his age? Not even twelve,' said Joe.

Then she was calling her mother.

'Mother, come here while we tell you what Jude said.'

Jude fled, his face flaming, towards a green field, as if he was being pursued. He threw himself on the grass. Nobody could find him. He turned on his back and looked at the sky. It was darkening already. There were colours around its edges.

They don't understand, he raged, gripping the grass with his fingers. How could you make them understand and not to be laughing? He remembered going into his sister's room for the pennies. She had covered herself up. She was a girl too, see. Before it had made no difference. Now things were changed. They would never be the same. Never again.

Walter Macken is an Irish writer, born in Galaway in 1917. He died in 1967. He began his career as an actor in the Gallaway Gaelic theatre and had a substantial role in the film version of Brendan Behan's *The Quare Fellow*. He has written about Irish history in a trilogy of novels, *Seek the Fair Land, The Silent People* and *The Scorching Wind*. His short stories were frequently published in *The New Yorker*. Collections of his stories include: *Coll Doll* (Pan, 1976) and *God Made Sunday* (Pan, 1973).

Don: the True Story of a Young Person

■ *by Garrison Keillor* ■

Earl and Mavis Beeman and son Don, seventeen, had lived together in the two-bedroom green-stucco house at 2813 Rochester
for sixteen years, but for the last two they had been like ships in
the night. Don, a gangly youth with his father's large head and
flat nose and his mother's shoulder-length hair, kept to himself
and seldom spoke unless spoken to. 'Ever since he joined that
band . . . ' his dad said. Mavis suspected drugs and finally asked
Don straight out. He told her that coffee is a drug, but, as Mavis
pointed out, coffee drinkers do not lock themselves in their rooms
and never talk to their parents.

Actually, Don did love his folks. It was just that right now he
was totally into his music. But they thought something was wrong.
One Friday night, when Don and his band, Trash, were playing
for a dance at the Armory, Earl and Mavis went in and shook
down his room. Under the bed they found a box of tapes, num-
bered 1 through 4 and marked Songs. They played them and
found out they were songs written and sung by Don. They were
about subjects he had never discussed at home, such as anger and
violence. One song was about going down the street and tripping
up nuns, and although the Beemans were not Catholic, they were
shocked.

The next morning, Earl spoke to Don. He didn't mention the
songs, but he told Don to quit being moody around home and to
make good use of his time, instead of hanging around with a
bunch of punks who were up to no good. 'We didn't bring you
up to be just another dumb punk,' Earl told him. 'Sometimes you
make me ashamed to be your parent.'

Actually, punk rock, as it is called, has brought about some
useful changes in popular music, as many respected rock critics
have pointed out, and its roots can be traced back to the very
origins of rock itself and perhaps even a little bit farther. 'It goes
without saying,' Green Phillips has written in *Rip It Up: The
Sound of the American Urban Experience*, 'that punk rock is
outrageous. Outrage is its object, its *raison d'être*, its very soul.
It can also be said to be mean, filthy, stupid, self-destructive, and
a menace to society. But that does not mean we should minimise
its contribution or fail to see it for what it truly is: an attempt to
reject the empty posturing of the pseudo-intellectual album-ori-
ented Rock-as-Art consciousness cult of the post-*Pepper* era and
to recreate the primal persona of the Rocker as Car Thief, Drop-
out, and Guy Who Beats Up Creeps.'

Punk-rock bands, Phillips goes on to say, through their very
outrageousness – the musicians spitting onstage, cursing and

throwing things at the audience, breaking up dressing rooms, trying to burn down auditoriums, and sometimes seriously injuring their managers and road-crews – have forced many critics to re-examine certain pre-punk assumptions, such as the role of criticism.

As it turned out, criticism was exactly what Earl gave Don, especially after the President's Day County 4-H Poultry Show dance, at which Trash played. Actually, the dance wasn't so bad. The band was rowdy and yelled a lot of tough, punk types of stuff at the audience, but that was their thing, after all, and nobody really minded until Trash's drummer, Bobby Thompson, spat at Sharon Farley while she was being crowned Poultry Show Queen on the stage between numbers. He said that she had given him a stuck-up look, but Mrs Goodrich, the senior 4-H Club adviser, ordered him to leave the poultry barn instantly. But the kids thought it had been done just in fun, and yelled until she decided to let him stay, on condition that he didn't do any more of that sort of thing.

Of course, this was a direct challenge to the others in the band. Brian Bigelow, the bass player, spat at Mrs Goodrich as she left the stage, and then, with the crowd yelling and egging them on, the others in the band made belching noises and lifted up their shirts. Don and the other guitarist, Art Johnson, turned their amps up full blast, and soon feed pellets were flying back and forth. Things were just about completely out of hand when suddenly a guy tossed a chicken on the stage and Bobby grabbed it and bit its neck.

Instantly, the barn was hushed. 'Did you *see* that!' some people murmured. 'See *what*?' other people whispered. Trash packed up their equipment quickly, while several exhibitors chased and then caught the chicken. Somebody took it to a vet. Everyone went home.

The next morning at breakfast, Earl picked up the *Gazette* and found his son on page 1. '4-H DANCE ENDS IN RIOT AS ROCK BAND EATS LIVE BIRD,' the headline said. According to the story, police were investigating the incident, which one observer at the scene called 'an act of bestiality reminiscent of Nazi Germany.'

Earl, a veteran of the Second World War, exploded. He kicked open Don's bedroom door, flung himself at his son, who had only just awakened, and hauled him out of bed by one leg. 'Why?' he screamed. 'Why? Why? Why?' He swung wildly at the dumbfounded youth with the rolled-up newspaper.

'Why do you do everything possible to disgrace us?' he yelled.

'Why must you search for ways to show your hatred and contempt? Even if you have no respect for us, do you have no respect for yourself? How can you do this? Is there no limit?'

'Dad,' Don said when Earl finally paused for breath. 'Dad, it's only music.'

'It's only music,' Earl repeated dumbly. 'It's only music. You drag our name in the mud, and you say it's only music. I suppose the next thing you'll tell me is it's only a chicken!'

Actually, it *was* only a chicken, as Don and his friends kept telling each other when they met that night in Bobby's garage to rehearse. They hadn't shot a deer or gutted a fish or slaughtered a pig or thrown a lobster into a pot of boiling water. One of them, in the excitement of the moment, had simply bitten the neck of a chicken – a chicken that, as it turned out, was going to be perfectly O.K. They had the vet's word on that.

'They are trying to pin on us all the violence and hatred that are in their own hearts,' said Brian, hanging up his big bass speaker on a rafter. 'They think our music is violent just because it shows them where *they* are at and they don't dare to admit it.'

'They can try all they want but they'll never stop rock and roll,' Bobby said, referring to Mrs Goodrich, who had already called up all of the county 4-H Club advisers, several youth ministers, a lot of high school teachers, and the county extension agent to arrange an emergency meeting that night.

'TEEN LEADERS VOW ANTI-ROCK DRIVE, AIM SMUT BAN IN AREA,' the *Gazette* reported the following morning. 'Longtime youth worker Diane Goodrich enjoys having a good time as much as the next person [the story went on], but Monday night, watching a local rock band rip into a live chicken with their teeth at the 4-H Poultry Show dance, she decided it was time to call "foul." Evidently, more than a few people agree with her. Last night, at a meeting in the high school auditorium attended on a word-of-mouth basis by literally dozens of parents, not to mention civic leaders and youth advisers, she spoke for the conscience of a community when she said, "Have we become so tolerant of deviant behaviour, so sympathetic toward the sick of our society, that, in the words of Bertram Follette, we have lost the capacity to say, This is not far out. You have simply gone too far. Now we say No!?" '

Don walked slowly home from school that day. A 'B+' student, he was sensitive to the accusations made against him and his

52

friends, and while he knew that the uproar had been caused at least partly by irresponsible reporting in the media, he also realised that the time had come for both sides to cool the rhetoric and sit down and talk. In his mind, he sought ways for his dad and himself to resolve their differences, but he couldn't think of a single one. Actually, their relationship had been pretty good – at least, on a hunting-and-fishing level. Earl had taught Don how to handle a shotgun and tie a fly and clean a fish and take care of a skillet and, most of all, how to sit still all morning in the blind. Actually, that was a problem. In hunting and fishing, it is important, of course, to be absolutely quiet. Don and Earl had spent whole days on Stone Lake casting into rocky inlets for bass, and if Don so much as rattled an oarlock Earl glared at him. Don was never encouraged to share with his dad his feelings about himself or his hopes for the future. He was expected to sit and not scare fish.

It was a shaken Trash, an incensed Trash, that met in the Thompsons' garage after supper on Wednesday. 'We're going to show them,' Brian vowed, his fists clenched white, 'that we can be everything they say we are. They tell lies about us – O.K., we're going to make those lies come true!'

That night, they played with wild abandon. The garage windows rattled as the band members blew off their frustration at having been attacked for something that had been blown up way out of proportion.

> Baby, you call me an animal for
> something I didn't do,
> Well, if that's how you want it
> I'm going to be wild for you!

At the word 'wild,' the boys lunged forward and crouched and grinned like madmen.

> Well, O.K., baby, you think you're
> Little Red Riding Hood,
> I'll be the Big Bad Wolf, and this
> time I'll get you good.

Here, Art stomped on the blitz pedal, throwing his amp into overdrive, while Don beat on his Ripley B-19 with windmill chops, and Brian actually straddled the bass and rode it like a horse.

53

Bobby leaped from the drums and, with one yank, started up his father's lawn mower, to which they had taped a microphone.

> I'm gonna ride my mower all
> around this town,
> Cut everybody who's been trying to
> put me down!

Now they moved into the finale. The lawn mower was stopped and the band fell silent, except for the *bump-bump-bump* of Brian's bass, as Bobby staggered forward like somebody completely out of his mind – panting, groping, and stumbling, with his eyes wild – while Brian sang:

> Well, you call us trash, so what
> do we have to lose?
> We're gonna be so bad you can
> read it in the morning news!

Suddenly Bobby leaped into the air, rushed forward, reached into a cardboard box, and grabbed a chicken and bit it again and again, until the feathers flew.

Actually, it was just a pillow they had put there for the rehearsal, but it seemed real to Trash, who sat back exhausted after the song. They all had experienced a tremendous release from it, and yet they were stunned at what had happened.

'Like I wasn't even aware of what I was doing,' Bobby said. 'I couldn't believe it was me. It was that great.'

'It's bigger than us,' Art said. 'I get into it and I am just completely blown away.'

'I don't know if we should actually ever do it,' Don said. 'If you think we really should, then I guess so, but I really don't know.'

'I don't think we should do it unless we're really into it, but if it's going to happen, then I say let it happen,' Brian said.

On Wednesday evening, Earl and Mavis were sitting in their forest-green lounger chairs beside the fireplace in the basement family room, reading the sports and family sections, respectively, of the *Gazette*. There was more about Mrs Goodrich and her Committee for Teen Decency on the family page ('ROCK-RECORD ROAST SLATED FOR SUNDAY'), but by now Mavis was able to read articles on the subject without tears. 'I don't know, I feel they are being unfair to Don and his friends,' she said to Earl. 'They are making a mountain out of what was probably just a joke. Mrs Thompson told me that Bobby didn't even draw blood on that chicken. All it suffered was a slight neck sprain. She said that when Bobby was little he would tease his sister by pretending to eat angleworms. Maybe this is the same thing.'

'Time they grew up, then,' Earl said. 'They walk around like they got the world on a string. Never listen to a thing you say. Treat you like dirt. Maybe this'll give them a taste of their own medicine.'

'I don't know,' Mavis said thoughtfully. 'A mother doesn't have all the answers. Sometimes I'm upset by little things they do or say. Sometimes I wonder. But in the end I know he's still my boy. I may not always understand, but I know he needs me to be here, to listen, to forgive. And I know there's nobody so bad but what they deserve a second chance.'

Earl and Mavis talked a long time that night. They remembered the many good times they had had with Don – the pleasure he had given them, the many wonderful memories. Mavis recalled that Don's first word had been Papa, and Earl recalled that his second was chicken. They both had a good laugh over that!

'They were good years, Mave,' Earl said, his eyes glistening. 'I've been wrong about Don. I'll do better now.'

'Tomorrow is a new day,' she replied brightly.

'He's a good boy if only we'd give him a chance,' said Earl, practically weeping.

'Just like his daddy,' said Mavis, reaching for his hand.

'Let's go up to bed,' said Earl, rising. He held her tightly.

'I think this is just going to bring us closer together,' she said.

Don couldn't sleep Wednesday night. He had gotten up twice, once to swipe a pack of his dad's Salems and then to get the blackberry wine left over from Christmas, and now, as he lay in bed drinking and smoking and carefully exhaling toward the fan that hummed in the window, he felt torn between his deep love of music and his fears that Trash was going off the deep end. He had confessed this doubt to Brian at school, and Brian said, 'If it feels good, then what's wrong?' Don was not completely certain in his own mind if this made sense or not. How can you feel good if you don't know it's right, he wondered. And how do you know if something is right?

After talking to Brian, he spent his lunch hour in the library, searching the short shelf marked Philosophy & Religion for a book that might clarify his thinking, and now he reached for it on the bedside table. It was *The Art of Decision-Making*, by M. Henry Fellows. A paragraph from the preface had impressed him, and now he read it again:

In a society appearing often paralysed by an overload of complex decisions, the act of decision-making may assume primary importance over the actual meaning and effect of the decision itself; or, to put it another way, a crucial function of the decision-making process is to assert the power to decide. It is necessary to make this point absolutely clear: in an increasingly complicated society, the act of making decisions is clearly not a matter of choice but a matter of necessity.

Once again Don knew he must decide whether to stay in Trash and risk banishment from home and the permanent hatred of a community (and perhaps a nation) united in outrage at the senseless injury (or even death) of a barnyard fowl, or not, and he had to decide before their next public appearance.

The next morning, Mavis got on the phone to the other Trash parents, and that evening, in the Beeman living room, the eight of them agreed that the boys had been treated unfairly and deserved a second chance. 'Let's put on a dance ourselves!' Art's mom suggested, and everybody said, 'Why not?' That week, Earl arranged through his union to rent the Bricklayers Hall for a low rate, and Mrs Thompson, who worked for an ad agency, formed her media friends into a publicity committee. Mavis took charge of refreshments, and Mr Thompson talked the mayor, an old fishing buddy, into granting them a provisional dance permit. 'We'll have to move fast before the City Council can rescind it,' he said. 'Saturday night's the night.'

Trash rehearsed Thursday night in the Thompsons' garage. Although they knew their folks had gotten behind them, they didn't discuss the planned dance, now tentatively titled (Mrs Thompson's idea) A Salute to Youth. Perhaps they couldn't believe it was true. Once again the music was so powerful, so all-encompassing, that the boys got carried away and went right into 'They Call Us Trash.' 'Let's not do that song tonight,' Don had asked, but they did – they couldn't help it – and they played even more wildly than before, perhaps because of a strobe light that Art had borrowed from his dad, a mechanic, who used it for balancing wheels. The effect of the strobe was frightening. Bobby ate practically half the pillow before they could get it away from him. They had to sit on him and hold him down, even though they were pretty shaky themselves. When they had quietened down a little, they tried out Brian's new song, which he had written that day:

All my life you told me 'Shut
     up and behave.'
Well, from now on, Mama, your
     boy's gonna scream and rave.

I know you hate to see me playing
     rock and roll,
But Mom, I gotta break your
     heart to save my soul.

Later on, Don would remember the last line as the point at which he had begun to make his decision.

Don came home from school Friday and, as usual, put on a record and fixed himself a peanut-butter-on-toast sandwich and a glass of milk. The phone rang just as the toast popped up. 'Long distance calling for a Donald Beeman,' said an operator's voice.
     'This is him,' Don answered.
     'Go ahead,' she said.
     'Don,' said a deep voice at the other end. 'Green Phillips here, at *Falling Rocks.*'
     Falling Rocks! At the mention of the name of the country's leading rock tabloid, Don's mind went completely numb. *Falling Rocks!* But –
     'Don, we have a photographer who is flying out there right now on a chartered jet to cover your concert tomorrow,' Phillips went on. 'I'll be doing the story from here, and I need something from you over the phone. I'm going upstairs in a minute and I'm going to try to sell this thing as a cover story, but at the moment I'm up against a Beatles-reunion rumour and a Phil Spector retrospective and God knows what else, so I need something to put us over the top. Don, I'm going to put it straight to you. I'm up against a bunch of editors who don't know what's going on, and I need to know something right now – not tonight, not tomorrow morning, not maybe, but yes or no. Is your guy going to eat the chicken or isn't he?'

'*What did you tell him?*' Bobby grabbed Don's shoulders and shook him and hugged him at the same time.

'I said probably.'

'*Probably?*'

'I said yes, I was pretty sure, it looked like that was going to happen.'

'It's in the *bank*!' Bobby yelled. 'It's not *going* to happen. It's *happening*!'

'Geek Rock is a style that departs radically from the punk genre even as it transcends it,' Green Phillips explained in the cover story he typed out that night. 'It is music with a mythic urge, raw and dirty and yet soaring off into the cosmic carny spirit of primitivist America and the sawdust world of the freak show of the soul, starring Tamar, Half Girl and Half Gorilla, and Koko, the Wild Man from Borneo Who Eats Live Spiders.

'For all the macho leather and scarred brilliance of its Presleys, Vincents, or Coopers,' he wrote, 'rock has always stayed within the bounds of urban sensibility – a more ordered world that has filed rebellion and outrage into the thematic grid of heavy drinking, hard fighting, hot cars, and fast sex. The achievement of Trash is to take us, as punk rock never can, into the darkest backroads of the heartland, back into the sideshow tent of the American expeience, and, inevitably, of course back into ourselves.'

On Saturday morning, Don slept late, and when he awoke he longed to go downstairs and plead with his mom and dad. 'Please cancel A Salute to Youth. Don't ask why – just cancel it immediately,' he wanted to tell them. But he knew it was too late for reappraisal. Whatever was going to happen had gained too much momentum.

The three hundred friends and relatives of Trash who jammed the Bricklayers Hall that night (including a number of ministers who believed that the basic message of rock was caring and sharing, as well as Don's grandma, who was hard of hearing) knew no such trepidation. They piled into the hall as if they were going to a party. It took Mr Thompson, who was master of ceremonies, several minutes to get all the people to take their seats and give him their attention. He spoke briefly on the importance of trust in human relationships and then, to brighten the occasion with a little humor, he shouted, 'And now, back *safe and sound* from its last engagement . . . ' and waved toward the wings, and out came the treasurer of the 4-H Club bearing a chicken with a bandaged neck. He put it down in its cage at the front of the stage, and the crowd gave the chicken a standing ovation.

Trash leaped out onstage, ready to play for keeps. 'We Come to Rock,' 'Look Out, Danger,' 'Electric Curtains,' 'It Hurts Me More,' and 'Dirty, Desperate, Born to Die' (all originals) led off the show and were appreciated by almost everyone. Many people in the crowd, including all the Trash parents, got up to dance to the crackling beat, which seemed to pound up through the floor. Some of the parents had learned this particular dance in adult-education classes. 'They certainly do get quite a sound out of secondhand instruments!' Mrs Thompson called to Mavis Beeman. Mavis was nervous. 'Don't they look a little feverish to you?' she asked. Don had actually been feeling sick all day. His face was flushed and his stomach was upset, but he had refused to let his mother take his temperature. 'Nothing at all,' he said when she asked what was wrong. But later he came into the kitchen during supper and said maybe it would be better if she and Earl stayed home tonight, that it might be too late for them.

'Of course not,' she had said. 'We *want* to be there.'

Now it was eleven o'clock – they had promised the Bricklayers to be through by eleven-thirty – and, standing at the back of the hall, trying to see over the dancers, Mavis was stricken by the sight of the chicken, still up there in its cage. She didn't know why, but she felt sure that if she could only reach the stage in time . . . 'Stop the music!' she cried. She pushed forward into the waves and currents of bodies, which shoved and battered against her as the band sang, 'You call me an animal for something I didn't do.'

'Don, it's not too late!' she hollered, but it was, and her efforts only served to give her a front-row seat for a sight she would never forget the rest of her life: a brief moment of eye contact with a chicken as it fixed her with an expression of utter reproach in the split second before Bobby tore open the cage.

'Perhaps no bird, not even the eagle, bluebird, or robin, has entered so deeply the folk consciousness of the race as has the common chicken (*Gallus gallus*),' Green Phillips had written. 'Indeed, throughout the Christian world, and even in many non-Christian countries, the chicken, from Plymouth Rock to lowly Leghorn, has come to stand for industry, patience, and fecundity, and, through its egg, for life itself, rebirth, and the resurrection of Christ, and, through its soup, for magical healing and restoration of the spirit. And yet, even as the chicken rides high as

59

symbol of the Right Life in the pastoral dreams of the post-agrarian bourgeoisie, its name has attracted other connotations – of pettiness, timidity, and foolishness – perhaps reflecting our culture's doubts about itself. It is the peculiar genius of Trash to exploit this dichotomy to its fullest resolution, and thus to release in an audience such revulsion as can only indicate that profound depths have been reached.'

Trash spent Saturday night at the Thompsons'. Mrs Thompson had said that she would not speak to them but she would not turn them away, either, and they were welcome to sleep in the basement. Mr Thompson was out consoling the Beemans, who had taken it hard, especially Mavis. Don called home Sunday afternoon, and his mom hung up on him.

Trash spent Sunday night on a bus to Omaha and put up at a Holiday Inn, and on Monday night played one set as an opening act to Sump, at the Armory. Advance ticket sales had been sluggish for weeks, until the promoter booked Trash on the strength of a page 2 photo in the Sunday paper showing Bobby with a faceful of feathers under the headline 'CHICKEN SLAIN BY MIDWEST SINGER.' Quickly reprinted on posters, it boosted box office some, but in the drafty hall, playing on borrowed gear to a strange and scattered audience, Trash couldn't work up to the emotional peak they needed to make the whole thing work. The new chicken sat in its cage and shivered, and when the time came Bobby hadn't the heart to do more that just pick it up and shake it. The crowd, which naturally expected more, booed them off the stage.

But actually it wasn't bad for starters. They got six hundred dollars for the night's work and a telephone call offering them a job in Tampa as opening act for the Ronnies, a successful band that already had an album, *Greatest Hits*, and was already popular in some places, including Wilkes-Barre, Gary, Erie, Louisville, and Baton Rouge. The Ronnies, who were into a combination of punk and heavy metal plus some middle of the road along with jazz, liked some of Trash's music O.K., but they were really turned on by the idea of the chicken bit. When they all met in Tampa to rehearse, the Ronnies cut Trash's set down to three songs and worked up a fifteen-minute routine for the chicken, with strobes and costumes and choreography and a truckload of chicken feathers to dump on the audience at the end. Bobby had to rehearse the chicken bit fourteen times that afternoon, but the Ronnies' manager, a little guy named Darrell Prince, was still not satisfied.

Bobby sort of seemed to have lost interest in the whole idea. 'I don't know,' he said. 'I really don't know.'

That night, before Trash's first show with the Ronnies, Darrell Prince came up to Don in the dressing room. 'You're doing the chicken,' he said to him.

'I don't know,' Don said. 'To tell you the truth, I've never done it before.'

'You watched the other kid do it. Just do what he did.'

'Well, to be perfectly honest with you, it's not actually something that I am particularly into right now.'

'*Get* into it,' the guy said, and he talked to Don for several minutes about rock and roll as a ritual expression of tribal unity which sets free powerful feelings, including anger and guilt, that require a blood sacrifice to restore the inner peace and harmony of the tribe. He gave examples of this from Mayan and early Japanese cultures, the Old Testament, NFL Sunday football, and the Spanish bullring. 'Besides,' he said, 'it's only a chicken.'

'I don't know,' Don said. 'I honestly don't think I could do it that *well*. People pay four, five dollars to get in, they deserve to see a good show. I might just get sick, or something.'

But Darrell Prince walked away, and a few minutes later Don and the rest of his friends were standing in a corridor of the amphitheatre ready to go on, and there was another chicken in a cage, and they could all hear the sounds of the crowd, which was already whistling and clapping for them to come out. Don did feel sick, and he didn't know if he was going to be able to do it or not. While he waited, he thought to himself that if just by doing it and feeling sick about doing it he would do some good, perhaps by showing any kids that might be in the audience that they should not try to do this, and that maybe it would be an example to them about violence. And besides, that afternoon the *Falling Rocks* story had come out, and they were some sort of stars.

Garrison Keillor was born in Minnesota. His stories with their homespun philosophy and small town gossip reflect the values of the Mid-West of America. His tales of Lake Woebegone are collected in *Lake Woebegone Days* (1986) and *Leaving Home* (1987). Many of them were originally written for the radio. They form a comic but revealing guide to the preoccupations of the small town-dweller.

A Piece of Pie
■ *by Damon Runyon* ■

On Boylston Street, in the city of Boston, Mass., there is a joint where you can get as nice a broiled lobster as anybody ever slaps a lip over, and who is in there one evening partaking of this titbit but a character by the name of Horse Thief and me.

This Horse Thief is called Horsey for short, and he is not called by this name because he ever steals a horse but because it is the consensus of public opinion from coast to coast that he may steal one if the opportunity presents.

Personally, I consider Horsey a very fine character, because any time he is holding anything he is willing to share his good fortune with one and all, and at this time in Boston he is holding plenty. It is the time we make the race meeting at Suffolk Down, and Horsey gets to going very good, indeed, and in fact he is now a character of means, and is my host against the broiled lobster.

Well, at a table next to us are four or five characters who all seem to be well-dressed, and stout-set, and red-faced, and prosperous-looking, and who all speak with the true Boston accent, which consists of many ah's and very few r's. Characters such as these are familiar to anybody who is ever in Boston very much, and they are bound to be politicians, retired cops, or contractors, because Boston is really quite infested with characters of this nature.

I am paying no attention to them, because they are drinking local ale, and talking loud, and long ago I learn that when a Boston character is engaged in aleing himself up, it is a good idea to let him alone, because the best you can get out of him is maybe a boff on the beezer. But Horsey is in there on the old Ear-ie, and very much interested in their conversation, and finally I listen myself just to hear what is attracting his attention, when one of the characters speaks as follows:

'Well,' he says, 'I am willing to bet ten thousand dollars that he can outeat anybody in the United States any time.'

Now at this, Horsey gets right up and steps over to the table and bows and smiles in a friendly way on one and all, and says:

'Gentlemen,' he says, 'pardon the intrusion, and excuse me for billing in, but,' he says, 'do I understand you are speaking of a great eater who resides in your fair city?'

Well, these Boston characters all gaze at Horsey in such a hostile manner that I am expecting any one of them to get up and request him to let them miss him, but he keeps on bowing and smiling, and they can see that he is a gentleman, and finally one of them says:

'Yes,' he says, 'we are speaking of a character by the name of

Joel Duffle. He is without doubt the greatest eater alive. He just wins a unique wager. He bets a character from Bangor, Me., that he can eat a whole window display of oysters in this very restaurant, and he not only eats all the oysters but he then wishes to wager that he can also eat the shells, but,' he says, 'it seems that the character from Bangor, Me., unfortunately taps out on the first proposition and has nothing with which to bet on the second.'

'Very interesting,' Horsey says. 'Very interesting, if true, but,' he says, 'unless my ears deceive me, I hear one of you state that he is willing to wager ten thousand dollars on this eater of yours against anybody in the United States.'

'Your ears are perfect,' another of the Boston characters says. 'I state it, although,' he says, 'I admit it is a sort of figure of speech. But I state it all right,' he says, 'and never let it be said that a Conway ever pigs it on a betting proposition.'

'Well,' Horsey says, 'I do not have a tenner on me at the moment, but,' he says, 'I have here a thousand dollars to put up as a forfeit that I can produce a character who will outeat your party for ten thousand, and as much more as you care to put up.'

And with this, Horsey outs with a bundle of coarse notes and tosses it on the table, and right away one of the Boston characters, whose name turns out to be Carroll, slaps his hand on the money and says:

'Bet.'

Well, now this is prompt action to be sure, and if there is one thing I admire more than anything else, it is action, and I can see that these are characters of true sporting instincts and I commence wondering where I can raise a few dibs to take a piece of Horsey's proposition, because of course I know that he has nobody in mind to do the eating for his side but Nicely-Nicely Jones.

And knowing Nicely-Nicely Jones, I am prepared to wager all the money I can possibly raise that he can outeat anything that walks on two legs. In fact, I will take a chance on Nicely-Nicely against anything on four legs, except maybe an elephant, and at that he may give the elephant a photo finish.

I do not say that Nicely-Nicely is the greatest eater in all history, but what I do say is he belongs up there as a contender. In fact, Professor D, who is a professor in a college out West before he turns to playing the horses for a livelihood, and who makes a study of history in his time, says he will not be surprised but what Nicely-Nicely figures one-two.

Professor D says we must always remember that Nicely-Nicely

eats under the handicaps of modern civilisation, which require that an eater use a knife and fork, or anyway a knife, while in the old days eating with the hands was a popular custom and much faster. Professor D says he has no doubt that under the old rules Nicely-Nicely will hang up a record that will endure through the ages, but of course maybe Professor D overlays Nicely-Nicely somewhat.

Well, now that the match is agreed upon, naturally Horsey and the Boston characters begin discussing where it is to take place, and one of the Boston characters suggests a neutral ground, such as New London, Conn., or Providence, R.I., but Horsey holds out for New York, and it seems that Boston characters are always ready to visit New York, so he does not meet with any great opposition on this point.

They all agree on a date four weeks later so as to give the principals plenty of time to get ready, although Horsey and I know that this is really unnecessary as far as Nicely-Nicely is concerned, because one thing about him is he is always in condition to eat.

This Nicely-Nicely Jones is a character who is maybe five feet eight inches tall, and about five feet nine inches wide, and when he is in good shape he will weigh upward of two hundred and eighty-three pounds. He is a horse player by trade, and eating is really just a hobby, but he is undoubtedly a wonderful eater even when he is not hungry.

Well, as soon as Horsey and I return to New York, we hasten to Mindy's restaurant on Broadway and relate the bet Horsey makes in Boston, and right away so many citizens, including Mindy himself, wish to take a piece of the proposition that it is oversubscribed by a large sum in no time.

Then Mindy remarks that he does not see Nicely-Nicely Jones for a month of Sundays, and then everybody present remembers that they do not see Nicely-Nicely around lately, either, and this leads to a discussion of where Nicely-Nicely can be, although up to this moment if nobody sees Nicely-Nicely but once in the next ten years it will be considered sufficient.

Well, Willie the Worrier, who is a bookmaker by trade, is among those present, and he remembers that the last time he looks for Nicely-Nicely hoping to collect a marker of some years' standing, Nicely-Nicely is living at the Rest Hotel in West Forty-ninth Street, and nothing will do Horsey but I must go with him over to the Rest to make inquiry for Nicely-Nicely, and there we learn that he leaves a forwarding address away up on Morningside Heights in care of somebody by the name of Slocum.

So Horsey calls a short, and away we go to this address, which turns out to be a five-story walk-up apartment, and a card downstairs shows that Slocum lives on the top floor. It takes Horsey and me ten minutes to walk up the five flights as we are by no means accustomed to exercise of this nature, and when we finally reach a door marked Slocum, we are plumb tuckered out, and have to sit down on the top step and rest a while.

Then I ring the bell at this door marked Slocum, and who appears but a tall young Judy with black hair who is without doubt beautiful, but who is so skinny we have to look twice to see her, and when I ask her if she can give me any information about a party named Nicely-Nicely Jones, she says to me like this:

'I guess you mean Quentin,' she says. 'Yes,' she says, 'Quentin is here. Come in, gentlemen.'

So we step into an apartment, and as we do so a thin, sickly looking character gets up out of a chair by the window, and in a weak voice says good evening. It is a good evening, at that, so Horsey and I say good evening right back at him, very polite, and then we stand there waiting for Nicely-Nicely to appear, when the beautiful skinny young Judy says:

'Well,' she says, 'this is Mr Quentin Jones.'

Then Horsey and I take another swivel at the thin character, and we can see that it is nobody but Nicely-Nicely, at that, but the way he changes since we last observe him is practically shocking to us both, because he is undoubtedly all shrunk up. In fact, he looks as if he is about half what he is in his prime, and his face is pale and thin, and his eyes are away back in his head, and while we both shake hands with him it is some time before either of us is able to speak. Then Horsey finally says:

'Nicely,' he says, 'can we have a few words with you in private on a very important proposition?'

Well, at this, and before Nicely-Nicely can answer aye, yes or no, the beautiful skinny young Judy goes out of the room and slams a door behind her, and Nicely-Nicely says:

'My fiancée, Miss Hilda Slocum,' he says. 'She is a wonderful character. We are to be married as soon as I lose twenty pounds more. It will take a couple of weeks longer,' he says.

'My goodness gracious, Nicely,' Horsey says. 'What do you mean lose twenty pounds more? You are practically emaciated now. Are you just out of a sick bed, or what?'

'Why,' Nicely-Nicely says, 'certainly I am not out of a sick bed.

I am never healthier in my life. I am on a diet. I lose eighty-three pounds in two months, and am now down to two hundred. I feel great,' he says. 'It is all because of my fiancée, Miss Hilda Slocum. She rescues me from gluttony and obesity, or anyway,' Nicely-Nicely says, 'this is what Miss Hilda Slocum calls it. My, I feel good. I love Miss Hilda Slocum very much,' Nicely-Nicely says. 'It is a case of love at first sight on both sides the day we meet in the subway. I am wedged in one of the turnstile gates, and she kindly pushes on me from behind until I wiggle through. I can see she has a kind heart, so I date her up for a movie that night and propose to her while the newsreel is on. 'But,' Nicely-Nicely says, 'Hilda tells me at once that she will never marry a fat slob. She says I must put myself in her hands and she will reduce me by scientific methods and then she will become my ever-loving wife, but not before.

'So,' Nicely-Nicely says, 'I come to live here with Miss Hilda Slocum and her mother, so she can supervise my diet. Her mother is thinner than Hilda. And I surely feel great,' Nicely-Nicely says. 'Look,' he says.

And with this, he pulls out the waistband of his pants, and shows enough spare space to hide War Admiral in, but the effort seems to be a strain on him, and he has to sit down in his chair again.

'My goodness gracious,' Horsey says. 'What do you eat, Nicely?'

'Well,' Nicely-Nicely says, 'I eat anything that does not contain starch, but,' he says, 'of course everything worth eating contains starch, so I really do not each much of anything whatever. My fiancée, Miss Hilda Slocum, arranges my diet. She is an expert dietitian and runs a widely known department in a diet magazine by the name of *Let's Keep House*.'

Then Horsey tells Nicely-Nicely of how he is matched to eat against this Joel Duffle, of Boston, for a nice side bet, and how he has a forfeit of a thousand dollars already posted for appearance, and how many of Nicely-Nicely's admirers along Broadway are looking to win themselves out of all their troubles by betting on him, and at first Nicely-Nicely listens with great interest, and his eyes are shining like six bits, but then he becomes very sad, and says:

'It is no use, gentlemen,' he says. 'My fiancée, Miss Hilda Slocum, will never hear of me going off my diet even for a little while. Only yesterday I try to talk her into letting me have a little pumpernickel instead of toasted whole wheat bread, and she says if I even think of such a thing again, she will break our engagement. Horsey,' he says, 'do you ever eat toasted whole wheat bread for a month hand running? Toasted?' he says.

'No,' Horsey says. 'What I eat is nice, white French bread, and corn muffins, and hot biscuits with gravy on them.'

'Stop,' Nicely-Nicely says. 'You are eating yourself into an early grave, and, furthermore,' he says, 'you are breaking my heart. But,' he says, 'the more I think of my following depending on me in this emergency, the sadder it makes me feel to think I am unable to oblige them. However,' he says, 'let me call Miss Hilda Slocum in on an outside chance and see what her reactions to your proposition are.'

So we call Miss Hilda Slocum in, and Horsey explains our predicament in putting so much faith in Nicely-Nicely only to find him dieting, and Miss Hilda Slocum's reactions are to order Horsey and me out of the joint with instructions never to darken her door again, and when we are a block away we can still hear her voice speaking very firmly to Nicely-Nicely.

Well, personally, I figure this ends the matter, for I can see that Miss Hilda Slocum is a most determined character, indeed, and the chances are it does end it, at that, if Horsey does not happen to get a wonderful break.

He is at Belmont Park one afternoon, and he has a real good thing in a jump race, and when a brisk young character in a hard straw hat and eyeglasses comes along and asks him what he likes, Horsey mentions this good thing, figuring he will move himself in for a few dibs if the good thing connects.

Well, it connects all right, and the brisk young character is very grateful to Horsey for his information, and is giving him plenty of much-obliges, and nothing else, and Horsey is about to mention that they do not accept much-obliges at his hotel, when the brisk young character mentions that he is nobody but Mr McBurgle and that he is the editor of the *Let's Keep House* magazine, and for Horsey to drop in and see him any time he is around his way.

Naturally, Horsey remembers what Nicely-Nicely says about Miss Hilda Slocum working for this *Let's Keep House* magazine, and he relates the story of the eating contest to Mr McBurgle and asks him if he will kindly use his influence with Miss Hilda Slocum to get her to release Nicely-Nicely from his diet long enough for the contest. Then Horsey gives Mr McBurgle a tip on another winner, and Mr McBurgle must use plenty of influence on Miss Hilda Slocum at once, as the next day she calls Horsey up at his hotel before he is out of bed, and speaks to him as follows:

69

'Of course,' Miss Hilda Slocum says, 'I will never change my attitude about Quentin, but,' she says, 'I can appreciate that he feels very bad about you gentlemen relying on him and having to disappoint you. He feels that he lets you down, which is by no means true, but it weighs upon his mind. It is interfering with his diet.

'Now,' Miss Hilda Slocum says, 'I do not approve of your contest, because,' she says, 'it is placing a premium on gluttony, but I have a friend by the name of Miss Violette Shumberger who may answer your purpose. She is my dearest friend from childhood, but it is only because I love her dearly that this friendship endures. She is extremely fond of eating,' Miss Hilda Slocum says. 'In spite of my pleadings, and my warnings, and my own example, she persists in food. It is disgusting to me but I finally learn that it is no use arguing with her.

'She remains my dearest friend,' Miss Hilda Slocum says, 'though she continues her practice of eating, and I am informed that she is phenomenal in this respect. In fact,' she says, 'Nicely-Nicely tells me to say to you that if Miss Violette Shumberger can perform the eating exploits I relate to him from hearsay she is a lily. Good-bye,' Miss Hilda Slocum says. 'You cannot have Nicely-Nicely.'

Well, nobody cares much about this idea of a stand-in for Nicely-Nicely in such a situation, and especially a Judy that no one ever hears of before, and many citizens are in favour of pulling out of the contest altogether. But Horsey has his thousand-dollar forfeit to think of, and as no one can suggest anyone else, he finally arranges a personal meet with the Judy suggested by Miss Hilda Slocum.

He comes into Mindy's one evening with a female character who is so fat it is necessary to push three tables together to give her room for her lap, and it seems that this character is Miss Violette Shumberger. She weighs maybe two hundred and fifty pounds, but she is by no means an old Judy, and by no means bad-looking. She has a face the size of a town clock and enough chins for a fire escape, but she has a nice smile and pretty teeth, and a laugh that is so hearty it knocks the whipped cream off an order of strawberry shortcake on a table fifty feet away and arouses the indignation of a customer by the name of Goldstein who is about to consume same.

Well, Horsey's idea in bringing her into Mindy's is to get some kind of line on her eating form, and she is clocked by many experts when she starts putting on the hot meat, and it is agreed

70

by one and all that she is by no means a selling-plater. In fact, by the time she gets through, even Mindy admits she has plenty of class, and the upshot of it all is Miss Violette Shumberger is chosen to eat against Joel Duffle.

Maybe you hear something of this great eating contest that comes off in New York one night in the early summer of 1937. Of course eating contests are by no means anything new, and in fact they are quite an old-fashioned pastime in some sections of this country, such as the South and East, but this is the first big public contest of the kind in years, and it creates no little comment along Broadway.

In fact, there is some mention of it in the blats, and it is not a frivolous proposition in any respect, and more dough is wagered on it than any other eating contest in history, with Joel Duffle a 6 to 5 favourite over Miss Violette Shumberger all the way through.

This Joel Duffle comes to New York several days before the contest with the character by the name of Conway, and requests a meet with Miss Violette Shumberger to agree on the final details and who shows up with Miss Violette Shumberger as her coach and adviser but Nicely-Nicely Jones. He is even thinner and more peaked-looking than when Horsey and I see him last, but he says he feels great, and that he is within six pounds of his marriage to Miss Hilda Slocum.

Well, it seems that his presence is really due to Miss Hilda Slocum herself, because she says that after getting her dearest friend Miss Violette Shumberger into this jackpot, it is only fair to do all she can to help her win it, and the only way she can think of is to let Nicely-Nicely give Violette the benefit of his experience and advice.

But afterward we learn that what really happens is that this editor, Mr McBurgle, gets greatly interested in the contest, and when he discovers that in spite of his influence, Miss Hilda Slocum declines to permit Nicely-Nicely to personally compete, but puts in a pinch eater, he is quite indignant and insists on her letting Nicely-Nicely school Violette.

Furthermore we afterward learn that when Nicely-Nicely returns to the apartment on Morningside Heights after giving Violette a lesson, Miss Hilda Slocum always smells his breath to see if he indulges in any food during his absence.

Well, this Joel Duffle is a tall character with stooped shoulders, and a sad expression, and he does not look as if he can eat his way out of a tea shoppe, but as soon as he commences to discuss

71

the details of the contest, anybody can see that he knows what time it is in situations such as this. In fact, Nicely-Nicely says he can tell at once from the way Joel Duffle talks that he is a dangerous opponent, and he says while Miss Violette Shumberger impresses him as an improving eater, he is only sorry she does not have more seasoning.

This Joel Duffle suggests that the contest consist of twelve courses of strictly American food, each side to be allowed to pick six dishes, doing the picking in rotation, and specifying the weight and quantity of the course selected to any amount the contestant making the pick desires, and each course is to be divided for eating exactly in half, and after Miss Violette Shumberger and Nicely-Nicely whisper together a while, they say the terms are quite satisfactory.

Then Horsey tosses a coin for the first pick, and Joel Duffle say heads, and it is heads, and he chooses, as the first course, two quarts of ripe olives, twelve bunches of celery, and four pounds of shelled nuts, all this to be split fifty-fifty between them. Miss Violette Shumberger names twelve dozen cherry-stone clams as the second course, and Joel Duffle says two gallons of Philadelphia pepper-pot soup as the third.

Well, Miss Violette Shumberger and Nicely-Nicely whisper together again, and Violette puts in two five-pound striped bass, the heads and tails not to count in the eating, and Joel Duffle names a twenty-two pound roast turkey. Each vegetable is rated as one course, and Miss Violette Shumberger asks for twelve pounds of mashed potatoes with brown gravy. Joel Duffle says two dozen ears of corn on the cob, and Violette replies with two quarts of lima beans. Joel Duffle calls for twelve bunches of asparagus cooked in butter, and Violette mentions ten pounds of stewed new peas.

This gets them down to the salad, and it is Joel Duffle's play, so he says six pounds of mixed green salad with vinegar and oil dressing, and now Miss Violette Shumberger has the final selection, which is the dessert. She says it is a pumpkin pie, two feet across, and not less than three inches deep.

It is agreed that they must eat with knife, fork or spoon, but speed is not to count, and there is to be no time limit, except they cannot pause more than two consecutive minutes at any stage, except in case of hiccoughs. They can drink anything, and as much as they please, but liquids are not to count in the scoring. The decision is to be strictly on the amount of food consumed, and the judges are to take account of anything left on the plates after a course, but not of loose chewings on bosom or vest up to an ounce. The losing side is to pay for the food, and in case of a tie they are to eat it off immediately on ham and eggs only.

Well, the scene of this contest is the second-floor dining-room of Mindy's restaurant, which is closed to the general public for the occasion, and only parties immediately concerned in the contest are admitted. The contestants are seated on either side of a big table in the centre of the room, and each contestant has three waiters.

No talking and no rooting from the spectators is permitted, but of course in any eating contest the principals may speak to each other if they wish, though smart eaters never wish to do this, as talking only wastes energy, and about all they ever say to each other is please pass the mustard.

About fifty characters from Boston are present to witness the contest, and the same number of citizens of New York are admitted, and among them is this editor, Mr McBurgle, and he is around asking Horsey if he thinks Miss Violette Shumberger is as good a thing as the jumper at the race track.

Nicely-Nicely arrives on the scene quite early, and his appearance is really most distressing to his old friends and admirers, as by this time he is shy so much weight that he is a pitiful scene, to be sure, but he tells Horsey and me that he thinks Miss Violette Shumberger has a good chance.

'Of course,' he says, 'she is green. She does not know how to pace herself in competition. But,' he says, 'she has a wonderful style. I love to watch her eat. She likes the same things I do in the days when I am eating. She is a wonderful character too. Do you ever notice her smile?' Nicely-Nicely says.

'But,' he says, 'she is the dearest friend of my fiancée, Miss Hilda Slocum, so let us not speak of this. I try to get Hilda to come to see the contest, but she says it is repulsive. Well, anyway,' Nicely-Nicely says, 'I manage to borrow a few dibs, and am wagering on Miss Violette Shumberger. By the way,' he says, 'if you happen to think of it, notice her smile.'

Well, Nicely-Nicely takes a chair about ten feet behind Miss Violette Shumberger, which is as close as the judges will allow him, and he is warned by them that no coaching from the corners will be permitted, but of course Nicely-Nicely knows this rule as well as they do, and furthermore by this time his exertions seem to have left him without any more energy.

There are three judges, and they are all from neutral territory. One of these judges is a party from Baltimore, Md., by the name

73

of Packard, who runs a restaurant, and another is a party from Providence, R.I., by the name of Croppers, who is a sausage manufacturer. The third judge is an old Judy by the name of Mrs Rhubarb, who comes from Philadelphia, and once keeps an actors' boarding-house, and is considered an excellent judge of eaters.

Well, Mindy is the official starter, and at 8.30 p.m. sharp, when there is still much betting among the spectators, he outs with his watch, and says like this:

'Are you ready, Boston? Are you ready, New York?'

Miss Violette Shumberger and Joel Duffle both nod their heads, and Mindy says commence, and the contest is on, with Joel Duffle getting the jump at once on the celery and olives and nuts.

It is apparent that this Joel Duffle is one of these rough-and-tumble eaters that you can hear quite a distance off, especially on clams and soups. He is also an eyebrow eater, an eater whose eyebrows go up as high as the part in his hair as he eats, and this type of eater is undoubtedly very efficient.

In fact, the way Joel Duffle goes through the groceries down to the turkey causes the Broadway spectators some uneasiness, and they are whispering to each other that they only wish the old Nicely-Nicely is in there. But personally, I like the way Miss Violette Shumberger eats without undue excitement, and with great zest. She cannot keep close to Joel Duffle in the matter of speed in the early stages of the contest, as she seems to enjoy chewing her food, but I observe that as it goes along she pulls up on him, and I figure this is not because she is stepping up her pace, but because he is slowing down.

When the turkey finally comes on, and is split in two halves right down the middle, Miss Violette Shumberger looks greatly disappointed, and she speaks for the first time as follows:

'Why,' she says, 'where is the stuffing?'

Well, it seems that nobody mentions any stuffing for the turkey to the chef, so he does not make any stuffing, and Miss Violette Shumberger's disappointment is so plain to be seen that the confidence of the Boston characters is somewhat shaken. They can see that a Judy who can pack away as much fodder as Miss Violette Shumberger has to date, and then beef for stuffing, is really quite an eater.

In fact, Joel Duffle looks quite startled when he observes Miss Violette Shumberger's disappointment, and he gazes at her with great respect as she disposes of her share of the turkey, and the mashed potatoes, and one thing and another in such a manner that she moves up on the pumpkin pie on dead even terms with

74

him. In fact, there is little to choose betwen them at this point, although the judge from Baltimore is calling the attention of the other judges to a turkey leg that he claims Miss Violette Shumberger does not clean as neatly as Joel Duffle does his, but the other judges dismiss this as a technicality.

Then the waiters bring on the pumpkin pie, and it is without doubt quite a large pie, and in fact it is about the size of a manhole cover, and I can see that Joel Duffle is observing this pie with a strange expression on his face, although to tell the truth I do not care for the expression on Miss Violet Shumberger's face, either.

Well, the pie is cut in two dead centre, and one half is placed before Miss Violette Shumberger and the other half before Joel Duffle, and he does not take more than two bites before I see him loosen his waistband and take a big swig of water, and thinks I to myself, he is now down to a slow walk, and the pie will decide the whole heat, and I am only wishing I am able to wager a little more dough on Miss Violette Shumberger. But about this moment, and before she as much as touches her pie, all of a sudden Violette turns her head and motions to Nicely-Nicely to approach her, and as he approaches, she whispers in his ear.

Now at this, the Boston character by the name of Conway jumps up and claims a foul and several other Boston characters join him in this claim, and so does Joel Duffle, although afterwards even the Boston characters admit that Joel Duffle is no gentleman to make such a claim against a lady.

Well, there is some confusion over this, and the judges hold a conference, and they rule that there is certainly no foul in the actual eating that they can see, because Miss Violette Shumberger does not touch her pie so far.

But they say that whether it is a foul otherwise all depends on whether Miss Violette Shumberger is requesting advice on the contest from Nicely-Nicely and the judge from Providence, R.I., wishes to know if Nicely-Nicely will kindly relate what passes between him and Violette so they may make a decision.

'Why,' Nicely-Nicely says, 'all she asks me is can I get her another piece of pie when she finishes the one in front of her.'

Now at this, Joel Duffle throws down his knife, and pushes back his plate with all but two bites of his pie left on it, and says to the Boston characters like this:

'Gentlemen,' he says, 'I am licked. I cannot eat another mouthful. You must admit I put up a game battle, but,' he says, 'it is useless for me to go on against this Judy who is asking for more pie before she even starts on what is before her. I am almost dying as it is, and I do not wish to destroy myself in a hopeless effort. Gentlemen,' he says, 'she is not human.'

Well, of course this amounts to throwing in the old napkin and Nicely-Nicely stands up on his chair, and says:

'Three cheers for Miss Violette Shumberger!'

Then Nicely-Nicely gives the first cheer in person, but the effort overtaxes his strength, and he falls off the chair in a faint just as Joel Duffle collapses under the table, and the doctors at the Clinic Hospital are greatly baffled to receive, from the same address at the same time, one patient who is suffering from undernourishment, and another patient who is unconscious from over-eating.

Well, in the meantime, after the excitement subsides, and wagers are settled, we take Miss Violette Shumberger to the main floor in Mindy's for a midnight snack, and when she speaks of her wonderful triumph, she is disposed to give much credit to Nicely-Nicely Jones.

'You see,' Violette says, 'what I really whisper to him is that I am a goner. I whisper to him that I cannot possibly take one bite of the pie if my life depends on it, and if he has any bets down to try and hedge them off as quickly as possible.'

'I fear,' she says, 'that Nicely-Nicely will be greatly disappointed in my showing, but I have a confession to make to him when he gets out of the hospital. I forget about the contest,' Violette says, 'and eat my regular dinner of pig's knuckles and sauerkraut an hour before the contest starts and,' she says, 'I have no doubt this tends to affect my form somewhat. So,' she says, 'I owe everything to Nicely-Nicely's quick thinking.'

It is several weeks after the great eating contest that I run into Miss Hilda Slocum on Broadway and it seems to me that she looks much better nourished than the last time I see her, and when I mention this she says:

'Yes,' she says, 'I cease dieting. I learn my lesson,' she says. 'I learn that male characters do not appreciate anybody who tries to ward off surplus tissue. What male characters wish is substance. Why,' she says, 'only a week ago my editor, Mr McBurgle, tells me he will love to take me dancing if only I get something on me for him to take hold of. I am very fond of dancing,' she says.

'But,' I say, 'what of Nicely-Nicely Jones? I do not see him around lately.'

'Why,' Miss Hilda Slocum says, 'do you not hear what this cad does? Why, as soon as he is strong enough to leave the hospital, he elopes with my dearest friend, Miss Violette Shumberger, leaving me a note saying something about two souls with but a single thought. They are down in Florida running a barbecue stand, and,' she says, 'the chances are, eating like seven mules.'

'Miss Slocum,' I says, 'can I interest you in a portion of Mindy's chicken fricassee?'

'With dumplings?' Miss Hilda Slocum says. 'Yes,' she says, 'you can. Afterwards I have a date to go dancing with Mr McBurgle. I am crazy about dancing,' she says.

Damon Runyon (1884–1946) was an American journalist and sports columnist. He is also well-known for his short stories about sportsman and small time mobsters, which are distinguished by their original use of slang. These are collected in such volumes as *Guys and Dollo* (1032), whioh hao aloo boon cuocoocfully adaptod ac a stage and cinema musical, *Take it Easy* (1938), *Runyon à la Carte* (1944), and *Short Takes* (1946).

Gorilla, My Love

■ *by Toni Cade Bambara* ■

That was the year Hunca Bubba changed his name. Not a change up, but a change back, since Jefferson Winston Vale was the name in the first place. Which was news to me cause he'd been my Hunca Bubba my whole lifetime, since I couldn't manage Uncle to save my life. So far as I was concerned it was a change completely to somethin soundin very geographical weatherlike to me, like somethin you'd find in a almanac. Or somethin you'd run across when you sittin in the navigator seat with a wet thumb on the map crinkly in your lap, watchin the roads and signs so when Granddaddy Vale say 'Which way, Scout,' you got sense enough to say take the next exit or take a left or whatever it is. Not that Scout's my name. Just the name Granddaddy call whoever sittin in the navigator seat. Which is usually me cause I don't feature sittin in the back with the pecans. Now, you figure pecans all right to be sittin with. If you thinks so, that's your business. But they dusty sometime and make you cough. And they got a way of slidin around and dippin down sudden, like maybe a rat in the buckets. So if you scary like me, you sleep with the lights on and blame it on Baby Jason and, so as not to waste good electric, you study the maps. And that's how come I'm in the navigator seat most times and get to be called Scout.

So Hunca Bubba in the back with the pecans and Baby Jason, and he in love. And we got to hear all this stuff about this woman he in love with and all. Which really ain't enough to keep the mind alive, though Baby Jason got no better sense than to give his undivided attention and keep grabbin at the photograph which is just a picture of some skinny woman in a countrified dress with her hand shot up to her face like she shame fore cameras. But there's a movie house in the background which I ax about. Cause I am a movie freak from way back, even though it do get me in trouble sometime.

Like when me and Big Brood and Baby Jason was on our own last Easter and couldn't go to the Dorset cause we'd seen all the Three Stooges they was. And the RKO Hamilton was closed readying up for the Easter Pageant that night. And the West End, the Regun and the Sunset was too far, less we had grown-ups with us which we didn't. So we walk up Amsterdam Avenue to the Washington and *Gorilla, My Love* playin, they say, which suit me just fine, though the 'my love' part kinda drag Big Brood some. As for Baby Jason, shoot, like Granddaddy say, he'd follow me into the fiery furnace if I say come on. So we go in and get three bags of Havmore potato chips which not only are the best potato chips but the best bags for blowin up and bustin real loud so the matron come trottin down the aisle with her chunky self, flashin that flashlight dead in your eye so you can give her some lip, and if she answer back and you already finish seein the show anyway, why then you just turn the place out. Which I love to do, no lie. With Baby Jason kickin at the seat in front, egging me on, and Big Brood mumblin bout what fiercesome things we goin do. Which means me. Like when the big boys come up on us talking bout Lemme a nickel. It's me that hide the money. Or when the bad boys in the park take Big Brood's Spaudeen way from him. It's me that jump on they back and fight awhile. And it's me that turns out the show if the matron get too salty.

So the movie come on and right away it's this churchy music and clearly not about no gorilla. Bout Jesus. And I am ready to kill, not cause I got anything gainst Jesus. Just that when you fixed to watch a gorilla picture you don't wanna get messed around with Sunday School stuff. So I am mad. Besides, we see this raggedy old brown film *King of Kings* every year and enough's enough. Grown-ups figure they can treat you just anyhow. Which burns me up. There I am, my feet up and my Havmore potato chips really salty and crispy and two jawbreakers in my lap and the money safe in my shoe from the big boys, and here comes this Jesus stuff. So we all go wild. Yellin, booin, stompin and carryin on. Really to wake the man in the booth up there who musta went to sleep, and put on the wrong reels. But no, cause he holler down to shut up and then he turn the sound up so we really gotta holler like crazy to even hear ourselves good. And the matron ropes off the children section and flashes her light all over the place and we yell some more and some kids slip under the rope and run up and down the aisle just to show it take more than some dusty ole velvet rope to tie us down. And I'm flingin the kid in front of me's popcorn. And Baby Jason kickin seats. And it's really somethin. Then here come the big and bad matron, the one they let out in case of emergency. And she totin that flashlight like she gonna use it on somebody. This here the coloured matron Brandy and her friends call Thunderbuns. She do not play. She do not smile. So we shut up and watch the simple ass picture.

Which is not so simple as it is stupid. Cause I realise that just about anybody in my family is better than this god they always talkin about. My Daddy wouldn't stand for nobody treatin any of us that way. My Mama specially. And I can just see it now, Big Brood up there on the cross talkin bout Forgive them Daddy cause they don't know what they doin. And my Mama say Get down from there you big fool, whatcha think this is, playtime? And my Daddy yellin to Granddaddy to get him a ladder cause Big Brood actin the fool, his mother side of the family showin up. And my Mama and her sister Daisy jumpin on them Romans beatin them with they pocketbooks. And Hunca Bubba tellin them folks on they knees they better get out the way and go get some help or they goin to get trampled on. And Granddaddy Vale sayin Leave the boy alone, if that's what he wants to do with his life we ain't got nothin to say about it. Then Aunt Daisy givin him a taste of that pocketbook, fussin bout what a damn fool old man Granddaddy is. Then everybody jumpin in his chest like the time Uncle Clayton went in the army and come back with only one leg and Granddaddy say somethin stupid about that's life. And by this time Big Brood off the cross and in the park playin handball or skully or somethin. And the family in the kitchen throwin dishes at each other, screamin bout if you hadn't done this I wouldn't had to do that. And me in the parlour trying to do my arithmetic yellin Shut it off.

Which is what I was yellin all by myself which make me a sittin target for Thunderbuns. But when I yell We want our money back, that gets everybody in chorus. And the movie windin up with this heavenly cloud music and the smart-ass up there in his hole in the wall turns up the sound again to drown us out. There comes Bugs Bunny which we already seen so we know we been had. No gorilla my nuthin. And Big Brood say Awwww sheeet, we goin to see the manager and get our money back. And I know from this we business. So I brush the potato chips out of my hair which is where Baby Jason like to put em, and I march myself up the aisle to deal with the manager, who is a crook in the first place for lyin out there sayin *Gorilla, My Love* playin. And I never did like the man cause he oily and pasty at the same time like the bad guy in the serial, the one that got a hideout behind a push-button bookcase and play 'Moonlight Sonata' with gloves on. I knock on the door and I am furious. And I am alone, too. Cause Big Brood suddenly got to go so bad even though my Mama told us bout goin in them nasty bathrooms. And I hear him sigh like he disgusted when he get to the door and see only a little kid there. And now I'm really furious cause I get so tired grownups messin over kids just cause they little and can't take em to court. What is it, he say to me like I lost my mittens or wet on myself or am somebody's retarded child. When in reality I am the smartest kid P.S. 186 ever had in its whole lifetime and you can ax anybody. Even them teachers that don't like me cause

I won't sing them Southern songs or back off when they tell me my questions are out of order. And cause my Mama come up there in a minute when them teachers start playin the dozens behind coloured folks. She stalk in with her hat pulled down bad and that Persian lamb coat draped back over one hip on account of she got her fist planted there so she can talk that talk which gets us all hypnotised, and teacher be comin undone cause she know this could be her job and her behind cause Mama got pull with the Board and bad by her own self anyhow.

So I kick the door open wider and just walk right by him and sit down and tell the man about himself and that I want my money back and that goes for Baby Jason and Big Brood too. And he still trying to shuffle me out the door even though I'm sittin which shows him for the fool he is. Just like them teachers do fore they realise Mama like a stone on that spot and ain't backin up. So he ain't gettin up off the money. So I was forced to leave, takin the matches from under his ashtray, and set a fire under the candy stand, which closed the raggedy ole Washington down for a week. My Daddy had the suspect it was me cause Big Brood got a big mouth. But I explained right quick what the whole thing was about and I figured it was even-steven. Cause if you say Gorilla, My Love, you suppose to mean it. Just like when you say you goin to give me a party on my birthday, you gotta mean it. And if you say me and Baby Jason can go South pecan haulin with Granddaddy Vale, you better not be comin up with no stuff about the weather look uncertain or did you mop the bathroom or any other trickified business. I mean even gangsters in the movies say My word is my bond. So don't nobody get away with nothin far as I'm concerned. So Daddy put his belt back on. Cause that's the way I was raised. Like my Mama say in one of them situations when I won't back down, Okay Badbird, you right. Your point is well-taken. Not that Badbird my name, just what she say when she tired arguin and know I'm right. And Aunt Jo, who is the hardest head in the family and worse even than Aunt Daisy, she say, You absolutely right Miss Muffin, which also ain't my real name but the name she gave me one time when I got some medicine shot in my behind and wouldn't get up off her pillows for nothin. And even Granddaddy Vale – who got no memory to speak of, so sometime you can just plain lie to him, if you want to be like that – he say, Well if that's what I said, then that's it. But this name business was different they said. It wasn't like Hunca Bubba had gone back on his word or anything. Just that he was thinkin bout gettin married and was usin his real name now. Which ain't the way I saw it at all.

So there I am in the navigator seat. And I turn to him and just plain ole ax him. I mean I come right on out with it. No sense goin all around that barn the old folks talk about. And like my Mama say, Hazel – which is my real name and what she remembers to call me when she being serious – when you got somethin on your mind, speak up and let the chips fall where they may. And if anybody don't like it, tell em to come see your Mama. And Daddy look up from the paper and say, You hear your Mama good, Hazel. And tell em to come see me first. Like that. That's how I was raised.

So I turn clear round in the navigator seat and say, 'Look here, Hunca Bubba or Jefferson Windsong Vale or whatever your name is, you gonna marry this girl?'

'Sure am,' he say, all grins.

And I say, 'Member that time you was baby-sittin me when we lived at four-o-nine and there was this big snow and Mama and Daddy got held up in the country so you had to stay for two days?'

And he say, 'Sure do.'

'Well. You remember how you told me I was the cutest thing that ever walked the earth?'

'Oh, you were real cute when you were little,' he say, which is suppose to be funny. I am not laughin.

'Well. You remember what you said?'

And Granddaddy Vale squintin over the wheel and axin Which way, Scout. But Scout is busy and don't care if we all get lost for days.

'Watcha mean, Peaches?'

'My name is Hazel. And what I mean is you said you were going to marry me when I grew up. You were going to wait. That's what I mean, my dear Uncle Jefferson.' And he don't say nuthin. Just look at me real strange like he never saw me before in life. Like he lost in some weird town in the middle of night and lookin for directions and there's no one to ask. Like it was me that messed up the maps and turned the road posts round. 'Well, you said it, didn't you?' And Baby Jason lookin back and forth like we playin ping-pong. Only I ain't playin. I'm hurtin and I can hear that I am screamin. And Granddaddy Vale mumblin how we never gonna get to where we goin if I don't turn around and take my navigator job serious.

83

'Well, for cryin out loud, Hazel, you just a little girl. And I was just teasin.'

'And I was just teasin,' I say back just how he said it so he can hear what a terrible thing it is. Then I don't say nuthin. And he don't say nuthin. And Baby Jason don't say nuthin nohow. Then Granddaddy Vale speak up. 'Look here, Precious, it was Hunca Bubba what told you them things. This here, Jefferson Winston Vale.' And Hunca Bubba say, 'That's right. That was somebody else. I'm a new somebody.'

'You a lyin dawg,' I say, when I meant to say treacherous dog, but just couldn't get hold of the word. It slipped away from me. And I'm crying and crumplin down in the seat and just don't care. And Granddaddy say to hush and steps on the gas. And I'm losin my bearins and don't even know where to look on the map cause I can't see for cryin. And Baby Jason cryin too. Cause he is my blood brother and understands that we must stick together or be forever lost, what with grown-ups playing change-up and turnin you round every which way so bad. And don't even say they sorry.

Toni Cade Bambara was born in 1939 in Harlem, New York and now lives in Atlanta, Georgia. She has published two volumes of stories *Gorilla, My Love* (1972) and *The Sea Birds are Still Alive* (1982). She has also written a novel, *The Salt Eaters* (1980) and a book on the Atlanta murders *These Bones Are Not My Child*.
She has said that her purpose in her writing is to try to 'break words open and get at the bones'. The stories in her first collection are focused through the eyes of a young girl trying to make sense of the world in which she is growing up, those in her second are about young and middle-aged women. They all highlight the struggle to break out of the restrictions on personal freedom that arise from expectations about race and gender.

Rapunzstiltskin
■ *by Liz Lochhead* ■

& just when our maiden had got
good & used to her isolation,
stopped daily expecting to be rescued,
had come to almost love her tower,
along comes This Prince
with absolutely
all the wrong answers.
Of course she had not been brought up to look for
originality or gingerbread
so at first she was quite undaunted
by his tendency to talk in strung-together cliché.
'Just hang on and we'll get you out of there'
he hollered like a fireman in some soap opera
when she confided her plight (the old
hag inside etc, & how trapped she was);
well, it was corny but
he did look sort of gorgeous,
axe and all.
So there she was, humming & pulling
all the pins out of her chignon,
throwing him all the usual lifelines
till, soon, he was shimmying in & out
every other day as though
he owned the place, bringing her
the sex manuals & skeins of silk
from which she was meant, eventually,
to weave the means of her own escape.
'All very well & good,' she prompted,
'but when exactly?'
She gave him till
well past the bell on the timeclock.
She mouthed at him, hinted
she was keener than a TV quizmaster
that he should get it right.
'I'll do everything in my power' he intoned, 'but
the impossible (she groaned) might
take a little longer.' He grinned.
She pulled her glasses off.
'All the better
to see you with my dear?' he hazarded.
She screamed, cut off her hair.
'Why, you're beautiful?' he guessed tentatively.
'No. No. No!' she

86

shrieked & stamped her foot so
hard it sank six cubits through the floorboards,
'I love you?' he came up with,
as finally she tore herself in two.

Liz Lochhead is a Scottish playwright and poet, known as well for her performances as for the published collections of her poetry. She was born in Motherwell in 1947 and trained as a painter in Glasgow Art College before teaching for eight years. Her work is marked by her flair for telling and retelling stories.

Collections of her poetry are: *Memo for Spring, Islands* and *Grimm Sisters*; all collected in *Dreaming Frankenstein and Collected Poems* (Polygon, 1984).

The Glass Cupboard

■ *by Terry Jones* ■

There was once a cupboard that was made entirely of glass so you could see right into it and right through it. Now, although this cupboard always appeared to be empty, you could always take out whatever you wanted. If you wanted a cool drink, for example, you just opened the cupboard and took one out. Or if you wanted a new pair of shoes, you could always take a pair out of the glass cupboard. Even if you wanted a bag of gold, you just opened up the glass cupboard and took out a bag of gold. The only thing you had to remember was that, whenever you took something *out* of the glass cupboard, you had to put something else back *in*, although nobody quite knew why.

Naturally such a valuable thing as the glass cupboard belonged to a rich and powerful King.

One day, the King had to go on a long journey, and while he was gone some thieves broke into the palace and stole the glass cupboard.

'Now we can have anything we want,' they said.

One of the robbers said: 'I want a large bag of gold,' and he opened the glass cupboard and took out a large bag of gold.

Then the second robber said: 'I want two large bags of gold,' and he opened the glass cupboard and took out two large bags of gold.

Then the chief of the robbers said: 'I want three of the biggest bags of gold you've ever seen!' and he opened the glass cupboard and took out three of the biggest bags of gold you've ever seen.

'Hooray!' they said. 'Now we can take out as much gold as we like!'

Well, those three robbers stayed up the whole night, taking bag after bag of gold out of the glass cupboard. But not one of them put anything back in.

In the morning, the chief of the robbers said: 'Soon we shall be the richest three men in the world. But let us go to sleep now, and we can take out more gold tonight.'

So they lay down to sleep. But the first robber could not sleep. He kept thinking: 'If I went to the glass cupboard just *once* more, I'd be even richer than I am now.' So he got up, and went to the cupboard, and took out yet another bag of gold, and then went back to bed.

And the second robber could not sleep either. He kept thinking: 'If I went to the glass cupboard and took out two more bags of gold, I'd be even richer than the others.' So he got up, and went to the cupboard, and took out two more bags of gold, and then went back to bed.

Meanwhile the chief of the robbers could not sleep either. He kept thinking: 'If I went to the glass cupboard and took out three more bags of gold, I'd be the richest of all.' So he got up, and went to the cupboard, and took out three more bags of gold, and then went back to bed.

And then the first robber said to himself: 'What am I doing, lying here sleeping, when I could be getting richer?' So he got up, and started taking more and more bags of gold out of the cupboard.

The second robber heard him and thought: 'What am I doing, lying here sleeping, when he's getting richer than me?' So he got up and joined his companion.

And then the chief of the robbers got up too. 'I can't lie here sleeping,' he said, 'while the other two are both getting richer than me.' So got up and soon all three were hard at it, taking more and more bags of gold out of the cupboard.

And all that day and all that night not one of them dared to stop for fear that one of his companions would get richer than him. And they carried on all the next day and all the next night. They didn't stop to rest, and they didn't stop to eat, and they didn't even stop to drink. They kept taking out those bags of gold faster and faster and more and more until, at length, they grew faint with lack of sleep and food and drink, but still they did not dare to stop.

All that week and all the next week, and all that month and all that winter, they kept at it, until the chief of the robbers could bear it no longer, and he picked up a hammer and smashed the glass cupboard into a million pieces, and they all three gave a great cry and fell down dead on top of the huge mountain of gold they had taken out of the glass cupboard.

Sometime later the King returned home, and his servants threw themselves on their knees before him, and said: 'Forgive us, Your Majesty, but three wicked robbers have stolen the glass cupboard!'

The King ordered his servants to search the length and breadth of the land. When they found what was left of the glass cupboard, and the three robbers lying dead, they filled sixty great carts with all the gold and took it back to the King. And when the King heard that the glass cupboard was smashed into a million pieces and that the three thieves were dead, he shook his head and said: 'If those thieves had always put something back into the cupboard for every bag of gold they had taken out, they would be alive to this day.' And he ordered his servants to collect all the pieces of the glass cupboard and to melt them down and make them into a globe with all the countries of the world upon it, to remind himself, and others, that the earth is as fragile as that glass cupboard.

Terry Jones is widely known as a member of the Monty Python's Flying Circus team. He studied English Literature at Oxford and retains a fascination for all things medieval. This preoccupation is reflected both in his story-telling and his film-making. He began to write fairy stories to amuse his own daughter and they are at their best when read out loud. He has also written a more academic study of Chaucer's knight as well as children's stories such as *The Saga of Erio tho Viking* and *Nicobobinus*.

The Day They Burned the Books

■ by Jean Rhys ■

My friend Eddie was a small, thin boy. You could see the blue veins in his wrists and temples. People said that he had consumption and wasn't long for this world. I loved, but sometimes despised him.

His father, Mr Sawyer, was a strange man. Nobody could make out what he was doing in our part of the world at all. He was not a planter or a doctor or a lawyer or a banker. He didn't keep a store. He wasn't a schoolmaster or a government official. He wasn't – that was the point – a gentleman. We had several resident romantics who had fallen in love with the moon on the Caribees – they were all gentlemen and quite unlike Mr Sawyer who hadn't an 'h' in his composition. Besides, he detested the moon and everything else about the Caribbean and he didn't mind telling you so.

He was agent for a small steamship line which in those days linked up Venezuela and Trinidad with the smaller islands, but he couldn't make much out of that. He must have a private income, people decided, but they never decided why he had chosen to settle in a place he didn't like and to marry a coloured woman. Though a decent, respectable, nicely educated coloured woman, mind you.

Mrs Sawyer must have been very pretty once but, what with one thing and another, that was in days gone by.

When Mr Sawyer was drunk – this often happened – he used to be very rude to her. She never answered him.

'Look at the nigger showing off,' he would say; and she would smile as if she knew she ought to see the joke but couldn't. 'You damned, long-eyed gloomy half-caste, you don't smell right,' he would say; and she never answered, not even to whisper, 'You don't smell right to me, either.'

The story went that once they had ventured to give a dinner party and that when the servant, Mildred, was bringing in coffee, he had pulled Mrs Sawyer's hair. 'Not a wig, you see,' he bawled. Even then, if you can believe it, Mrs Sawyer had laughed and tried to pretend that it was all part of the joke, this mysterious, obscure, sacred English joke.

But Mildred told the other servants in the town that her eyes had gone wicked, like a soucriant's eyes, and that afterwards she had picked up some of the hair he pulled out and put it in an envelope, and that Mr Sawyer ought to look out (hair is obeah as well as hands).

Of course, Mrs Sawyer had her compensations. They lived in a very pleasant house in Hill Street. The garden was large and

93

they had a fine mango tree, which bore prolifically. The fruit was small, round, very sweet and juicy – a lovely red-and-yellow colour when it was ripe. Perhaps it was one of the compensations, I used to think.

Mr Sawyer built a room on to the back of this house. It was unpainted inside and the wood smelt very sweet. Bookshelves lined the walls. Every time the Royal Mail steamer came in it brought a package for him, and gradually the empty shelves filled.

Once I went there with Eddie to borrow *The Arabian Nights*. That was on a Saturday afternoon, one of those hot, still afternoons when you felt that everything had gone to sleep, even the water in the gutters. But Mrs Sawyer was not asleep. She put her head in at the door and looked at us, and I knew that she hated the room and hated the books.

It was Eddie with the pale blue eyes and straw-coloured hair – the living image of his father, though often as silent as his mother – who first infected me with doubts about 'home', meaning England. He would be so quiet when others who had never seen it – none of us had ever seen it – were talking about its delights, gesticulating freely as we talked – London, the beautiful, rosy-cheeked ladies, the theatres, the shops, the fog, the blazing coal fires in winter, the exotic food (whitebait eaten to the sound of violins), strawberries and cream – the word 'strawberries' always spoken with a guttural and throaty sound which we imagined to be the proper English pronunciation.

'I don't like strawberries,' Eddie said on one occasion.

'You *don't like* strawberries?'

'No, and I don't like daffodils either. Dad's always going on about them. He says they lick the flowers here into a cocked hat and I bet that's a lie.'

We were all too shocked to say, 'You don't know a thing about it.' We were so shocked that nobody spoke to him for the rest of the day. But I for one admired him. I also was tired of learning and reciting poems in praise of daffodils, and my relations with the few 'real' English boys and girls I had met were awkward. I had discovered that if I called myself English they would snub me haughtily: 'You're not English; you're a horrid colonial.' 'Well, I don't much want to be English,' I would say. 'It's much more fun to be French or Spanish or something like that – and, as a matter of fact, I am a bit.' Then I was too killingly funny, quite ridiculous. Not only a horrid colonial, but also ridiculous. Heads I win, tails you lose – that was the English. I had thought about all this, and thought hard, but I had never dared to tell anybody what I thought and I realised that Eddie had been very bold.

But he was bold, and stronger than you would think. For one thing, he never felt the heat; some coldness in his fair skin resisted it. He didn't burn red or brown, he didn't freckle much.

Hot days seemed to make him feel especially energetic. 'Now we'll run twice round the lawn and then you can pretend you're dying of thirst in the desert and that I'm an Arab chieftain bringing you water.'

'You must drink slowly,' he would say, 'for if you're very thirsty and you drink quickly you die.'

So I learnt the voluptuousness of drinking slowly when you are very thirsty – small mouthful by small mouthful, until the glass of pink, iced Coca-Cola was empty.

Just after my twelfth birthday Mr Sawyer died suddenly, and as Eddie's special friend I went to the funeral, wearing a new white dress. My straight hair was damped with sugar and water the night before and plaited into tight little plaits, so that it should be fluffy for the occasion.

When it was all over everybody said how nice Mrs Sawyer had looked, walking like a queen behind the coffin and crying her eyeballs out at the right moment, and wasn't Eddie a funny boy? He hadn't cried at all.

After this Eddie and I took possession of the room with the books. No one else ever entered it, except Mildred to sweep and dust in the mornings, and gradually the ghost of Mr Sawyer pulling Mrs Sawyer's hair faded though this took a little time. The blinds were always half-way down and going in out of the sun was like stepping into a pool of brown-green water. It was empty except for the bookshelves, a desk with a green baize top and a wicker rocking-chair.

'My room,' Eddie called it. 'My books,' he would say, 'my books.'

I don't know how long this lasted. I don't know whether it was weeks after Mr Sawyer's death or months after, that I see myself and Eddie in the room. But there we are and there, unexpectedly, are Mrs Sawyer and Mildred. Mrs Sawyer's mouth tight, her eyes pleased. She is pulling all the books out of the shelves and piling them into two heaps. The big, fat glossy ones – the good-looking ones, Mildred explains in a whisper – lie in one heap. The *Encyclopaedia Britannica*, *British Flowers*, *Birds and Beasts*, various histories, books with maps, Froude's *English in the West Indies* and so on – they are going to be sold. The unimportant books,

95

with paper covers or damaged covers or torn pages, lie in another heap. They are going to be burnt – yes, burnt.

Mildred's expression was extraordinary as she said that – half hugely delighted, half-shocked, even frightened. And as for Mrs Sawyer – well, I knew bad temper (I had often seen it), I knew rage, but this was hate. I recognised the difference at once and stared at her curiously. I edged closer to her so that I could see the titles of the books she was handling.

It was the poetry shelf. *Poems*, Lord Byron, *Poetical Works*, Milton, and so on. Vlung, vlung, vlung – all thrown into the heap that were to be sold. But a book by Christina Rossetti, though also bound in leather, went into the heap that was to be burnt, and by a flicker in Mrs Sawyer's eyes I knew that worse than men who wrote books were women who wrote books – infinitely worse. Men could be mercifully shot; women must be tortured.

Mrs Sawyer did not seem to notice that we were there, but she was breathing free and easy and her hands had got the rhythm of tearing and pitching. She looked beautiful, too – beautiful as the sky outside which was a very dark blue, or the mango tree, long sprays of brown and gold.

When Eddie said 'No', she did not even glance at him.

'No,' he said again in a high voice. 'Not that one. I was reading that one.'

She laughed and he rushed at her, his eyes starting out of his head, shrieking, 'Now I've got to hate you too. Now I hate you too.'

He snatched the book out of her hand and gave her a violent push. She fell into the rocking-chair.

Well, I wasn't going to be left out of all this, so I grabbed a book from the condemned pile and dived under Mildred's outstretched arm.

Then we were both in the garden. We ran along the path, bordered with crotons. We pelted down the path, though they did not follow us and we could hear Mildred laughing – kyah, kyah, kyah, kyah. As I ran I put the book I had taken into the loose front of my brown holland dress. It felt warm and alive.

When we got into the street we walked sedately, for we feared the black children's ridicule. I felt very happy, because I had saved this book and it was my book and I would read it from the beginning to the triumphant words 'The End'. But I was uneasy when I thought of Mrs Sawyer.

'What will she do?' I said.

'Nothing,' Eddie said. 'Not to me.'

He was white as a ghost in his sailor suit, a blue-white even in the setting sun, and his father's sneer was clamped on his face.

'But she'll tell your mother all sorts of lies about you,' he said. 'She's an awful liar. She can't make up a story to save her life, but she makes up lies about people all right.'

'My mother won't take any notice of her.' I said. Though I was not at all sure.

'Why not? Because she's . . . because she isn't white?'

Well, I knew the answer to that one. Whenever the subject was brought up – people's relations and whether they had a drop of coloured blood or whether they hadn't – my father would grow impatient and interrupt. 'Who's white?' he would say. 'Damned few.'

So I said, 'Who's white? Damned few.'

'You can go to the devil,' Eddie said. 'She's prettier than your mother. When she's asleep her mouth smiles and she has curling eyelashes and quantities and quantitites and *quantities* of hair.'

'Yes,' I said truthfully. 'She's prettier than my mother.'

It was a red sunset that evening, a huge, sad, frightening sunset.

'Look, let's go back,' I said. 'If you're sure she won't be vexed with you, let's go back. It'll be dark soon.'

At his gate he asked me not to go. 'Don't go yet, don't go yet.'

We sat under the mango tree and I was holding his hand when he began to cry. Drops fell on my hand like the water from the dripstone in the filter in our yard. Then I began to cry too and when I felt my own tears on my hand I thought, 'Now perhaps we're married.'

'Yes, certainly, now we're married,' I thought. But I didn't say anything. I didn't say a thing until I was sure he had stopped. Then I asked, 'What's your book?'

'It's *Kim*,' he said. 'But it got torn. It starts at page twenty now. What's the one you took?'

'I don't know; it's too dark to see,' I said.

When I got home I rushed into my bedroom and locked the door because I knew that this book was the most important thing that had ever happened to me and I did not want anybody to be there when I looked at it.

But I was very disappointed, because it was in French and seemed dull. *Fort Comme La Mort*, it was called. . . .

Jean Rhys, christened Ella Gwendolen Rhys (1890–1979), was born in Dominica and came to England as a schoolgirl in 1907. She spent most of her later life in Paris where she began her career as a writer. Her stories are collected in *Tigers are Better Looking* (1976) and *Sleep it off Lady*. Her most accessible novel is *Wide Sargasso Sea* (1966). It tells the story of the exploitation of a beautiful creole girl, the first wife of Mr Rochester (from *Jane Eyre*) who becomes mad and is kept locked away in the attic. Many of her short stories create a striking picture of remembered scenes from her youth.

Follow on

Before you start

There are many ways of reading a story. You may wish to listen while the teacher or, perhaps, someone in the class, who has had time to prepare the reading carefully, reads it aloud. You may want to read it through in small groups, sharing out roles and trying out some of the different accents and dialects appropriate to the characters in the stories. Sometimes, you may choose to read a story by yourself, jotting down ideas about the characters and themes and your responses to them.

In our classrooms, many of the ideas for talking and writing which follow on from reading stories are suggested by the pupils themselves, and much of the work we have included in the 'follow-on' section has arisen out of negotiating assignments either with groups or with individuals. In order to work in this way, it is a good idea to begin by forming as full a picture as you can of what the story is about and the way you, as a reader, respond to the events, people and ideas in an individual way. Try jotting down your personal responses in a journal or reading diary as you read.

To help you think through initial ideas we have suggested a series of preliminary questions which we have called 'Working with the story'. These are not usually intended to be worked through as written exercises but may be used to select possible starting points for your own response. They will help you to speculate about what might happen in the story and enable you to build a picture of the events, settings and characters involved. Those that involve making a prediction about some aspect of the story are obviously best tackled before you begin to read the story.

It is often a good idea after reading a story to consider the questions the story suggests to you first, using ours as a back-up if you run short of ideas. You will also be able to use these questions to shape a piece of writing that demonstrates your understanding of a particular story. All GCSE syllabuses ask for evidence of this kind of understanding in assessed coursework and the second section which we have called 'Reading between the lines' enables you to explore more fully the issues raised by individual stories.

When you have shared and compared your responses in class you may want to move on to the third section, 'Leaving the story behind'. The map of activities at the end of the 'follow-on' section will help you to choose a particular kind of writing or group task.

Once you have worked on individual stories you may want to look at the section 'Working with the anthology' to help you to consider also the collection as a whole. If thematic work interests you, we have suggested ideas for categorising and analysing the stories so that you can make your own connections between them.

This collection is not intended to be a coursework book; if you choose to read it from cover to cover without looking at our suggestions we will be delighted that you share our enthusiasm for a good read.

Everyday Use
by Alice Walker

Working with tho story

1   The title of this story suggests that it might be about any one of a number of things. Working in a group, see how many different ideas you can suggest for its possible content. You must provide a good reason for each choice. List your ideas on large sheets of paper which can be displayed on the classroom wall. Compare your ideas with those of other groups.

2   Who is telling the story? What is your impression of the storyteller's way of life from reading the first three paragraphs of the story?

3   Pick out particular details used to describe the two sisters, Maggie and Dee, in the story. Organise your work under three headings, setting it out in columns like this:

	Favourable	Unfavourable	Neutral
Maggie			
Dee			

- Using your chart as a starting point, write your own description of the two sisters. Bring out the contrasts between them and compare the different attitudes of the storyteller to each of her daughters.

4   Why do you think the story teller compares Maggie with 'a lame animal'? What else in the story supports this view of her?

5   Why is Dee's mother surprised by her elder daughter's appearance? What reasons are given for the change in her life-style and the names that she says have been 'given' to her and her friend?

6   Which objects in the house does Dee 'covet'? Explain why she would like to own them.

7   Now that you have finished thinking carefully about the story, you
    may have more to add to your ideas about the meaning of the
    title 'Everyday Use'. In your groups, refer back to the display you
    made before you read the story. Underline or highlight those
    ideas which most closely relate to Alice Walker's story.

Reading between the lines

1   We see the events of the story through one person's eyes.
    Choose any other person in the story and write the events from
    that point of view. Use the kind of language that you think suits
    the character.

2   Imagine you are Maggie explaining to your own daughter how
    you came to inherit the quilt and why it is important to you. This
    could be presented either as a dramatic monologue or as a letter.

Leaving the story behind

1   In this story the names people use are very important in revealing
    other things about their identity. In small groups, try to find out
    if names influence your feelings about a person's character, age
    and possible origins.

    Begin by sharing your feelings about your own name with the
    group, work round in a circle. For example, you might talk about
    whether or not you like your name, if you have ever tried to change
    it, whether you have a pet name or a nickname and, if so, who
    uses it.

    What assumptions do you make about people from their names?
    Discuss your response to other names, perhaps using a chart
    similar to the one below to start you off:

Name	Age	Occupation	Hobbies
Albert			
Tracey			

    Discuss the ways in which names can influence our judgements
    about people. What in your opinion are the dangers of this kind
    of stereotyping?

    As a piece of research find out about naming conventions in other
    cultures. Do people from other cultures have similar or different
    ways of interpreting names?

2 Find out about any 'treasures' that have been handed down in your family. If possible, bring the article to school. Often such treasures have stories attached to them. Working in pairs, share your stories and then write about your partner's treasured possession.

3 Taking one of the ideas from your work on the title, write your own story with the title, 'Everyday Use.'

4 Read the following poem:

Looking at quilts

Who decided what is useful in its beauty
means less than what has no function besides beauty
(except its weight in money)?
Art without frames: it held parched corn,
it covered the table where soup misted savour,
it covered the bed where the body knit
to self and other and the
dark wool of dreams

The love of the ordinary blazes out: the backyard
miracle: Ohio Sunflower,
                              Snail's Track,
                                        Sweet Gum Leaf,
            Moon over the Mountain.

In the pattern Tulip and Peony the sense
of design masters the essence of what sprawled
in the afternoon: called conventionalised
to render out the intelligence, the graphic wit.

Some have a wistful faded posy yearning:
                                        Star of the Four Winds,
            Star of the West,
                              Queen Charlotte's Crown.
In a crabbed humour as far from pompous
as a rolling pin, you can trace wrinkles
from smiling under a scorching grasshopper sun:
            Monkey Wrench,
                              The Drunkard's Path,
                                        Fool's Puzzle,
            Puss in the Corner,
                              Robbing Peter to Pay Paul,
and the deflating
                              Hearts and Gizzards.

103

Pieced quilts, patchwork from best gowns,
winter woollens, linens, blankets, worked jigsaw
of the memories of braided lives, precious
scraps: women were buried but their clothing wore on.

Out of death from childbirth at sixteen, hard
work at forty, out of love for the trumpet vine
and the melon, they issue to us:
                                Rocky Road to Kansas,
          Job's Troubles,
                    Crazy Ann,
                              The Double Irish Chain,
          The Tree of Life:
                         this quilt might be
the only perfect artifact a woman
would ever see, yet she did not doubt
what we had forgotten, that out of her
potatoes and colic, sawdust and blood
she could create; together, alone,
she seized her time and made new.

Marge Piercy

This poem describes the different patterns used by pioneering
American women when they were sewing quilts. See if you can find
out more about such work by research in the library. Quilts are now
bought for large sums of money and hung like paintings. They are
valued for their history, design and beauty rather than for their
everyday use. Write your own poem about something you value
which is both beautiful and useful.

Taping oral histories

If you wish to undertake this assignment you will need to be familiar
with the use of a cassette recorder and to practise taping before
you interview people.

It is also important for you to organise the structure of your interview
before you begin it. You will need to prepare questions that will
encourage the person you are going to interview to talk. Some
questions are better at doing this than others. For example, if you
ask a direct question such as, 'What was your job?', you may only
get a single word answer, 'A fitter.' Such questions are called
'closed' questions. If you ask a more 'open' question you will
encourage your subject to give you a more detailed response. For
example, you might ask, 'Could you tell me something about the work
you used to do?' or 'What aspects of your work did you enjoy most?'

Practise asking your friend the questions to see whether they are suitable for an interview. Review your recording to find out which of your questions produced fuller answers. When you are confident in using the recorder and asking questions, make arrangements for your interview. It is often better if two people work together so that one person asks the questions, while the other does the recording.

Interview an older member of your family or community about their memories of a more traditional way of life. This could be centred around a piece of memorabilia, for example, a photograph, an old-fashioned tool, a piece of clothing; or around recollections of another country such as Wales, Ireland, Trinidad, South Africa, Pakistan.

When you have recorded this information you will need to decide whether you want to transcribe your tape and use it for a piece of written work or edit it for playing to others. If you do not have editing facilities, the easiest way to do this is to select the most interesting answers to your questions and play them to the class, supplying your own commentary.

Wider reading

Everyday Use is taken from Alice Walker's collection *In Love and Trouble* (1984). You may wish to read more from this collection and some of her other stories in *You Can't Keep a Good Woman Down* (Women's Press, 1982).

Related reading

Other books on a similar topic which you may enjoy are:
I Know Why the Caged Bird Sings, Maya Angelou, (Students' Virago, 1988). (This edition also suggests further ideas for writing.)
Roots, Alex Haley, (Picador, 1978). The story of a black American's search for his African heritage.

Carrying on the theme of cultural traditions are:
The Fox in Winter, John Branfield (Collins Cascades, 1983).
Granny was a Buffer Girl, Berlie Doherty (Armada Lions, 1988).

A Chip of Glass Ruby

by Nadine Gordimer

Working with the story

1   From the details in the opening paragraphs what impression do
    you get of the system of government in the country in which this
    story is set?

2   For whom is Mrs Bamjee duplicating leaflets? What is surprising
    about her involvement in this cause?

3   In what ways does Mrs Bamjee behave as 'any Moslem woman
    should'? How is her behaviour different from that of other women
    of her religion?

4   Make a list of Mr Bamjee's actions and feelings in the days
    following the arrest of his wife. How do *you* feel about his response
    to the troubles?

5   How does Jimmy explain the coloured teacher's attitude to
    Ahmed? What do you think the reader is being shown about
    apartheid?

6   Reread the last paragraph of the story carefully and then look
    again at your answer to question 4. Has your view of the
    Bamjees' relationship changed in any way? Give your reasons.

Reading between the lines

One clue to the meaning of the story lies in Mrs Bamjee's abandoning
of the chip of glass ruby given to her by her mother. The title may
have greater meaning if you read the Old Testament description of
a good woman which you can find in Proverbs, chapter 31. It
contains these lines:

Who can find a virtuous woman for her price is
far above rubies?
The heart of her husband doth safely trust in her
so that he shall have no need of spoil.
She will do him good and not evil all the days of
her life.

● How far, do you think, this description fits Mrs Bamjee? Make a
  list of her good qualities and then some of the difficulties she
  creates for her family.
● Write about your view of Mrs Bamjee, bringing out her strengths
  as a wife and mother.

106

Leaving the story behind

1 Work in groups to pool information about apartheid and its enforcement in South Africa. Make a collection of newspaper cuttings and stories about South Africa.

Using your research material, write an essay that discusses the apartheid system. Some of the things you may wish to include are a historical account of its imposition, details of the current situation, the ban on international sporting links with South Africa, the attitude of other countries to the regime, as well as your own views.

2 Design the leaflet that Mrs Bamjee duplicates at home to encourage people to defy the pass laws.

3 Write a newspaper report of her arrest as it would be written in
* a newspaper that supports the actions of the South African government;
* the underground paper prepared by the group which Mrs Bamjee supports.

4 Have you ever wanted to protest about a particular case of injustice or discrimination?

Either write a song, poem, or a newspaper article which attempts to change other people's minds on such an issue.

Or write a letter to a person whose views on a particular issue you dislike. This may be someone with political power, like the Prime Minister or the leader of another country, or someone more closely connected with you, such as a teacher or parent.

5 Here is part of the speech made by Martin Ramokgadi at his trial for being a member of the African National Congress:

It is a well-known fact that South Africa is a very wealthy country. I came to realise that the blacks were to produce the wealth of this country, not for their own benefit but primarily for the benefit of the white people. The vast plantations of fruit in this country are planted and tended by the black people yet it is the white people who enjoy it while blacks cannot afford to buy it. The gold that has made this country is mined by us, and yet it is the white people who pocket the cash. The towering buildings that make the beautiful cities have been built by our hands, yet we may not live in them. We blacks have been reduced to hewers of wood and drawers of water. All the luxuries are destined for the whites. This situation has directly affected me as a black man.

Write a speech to persuade others of the need for action on any issue you feel strongly about.

107

Wider reading

This story is taken from *Six Feet in the Country*, (Penguin, 1982). It is based on events in South Africa in the 1950s, but the situation is equally relevant today. You may also wish to read more of Nadine Gordimer's stories in *Selected Stories* (1983).

Related reading

No Easy Walk to Freedom is the Black African leader, Nelson Mandela's own story. (Heinemann, African Writers' Series, 1986)
 Part of My Soul, Winnie Mandela, ed. Anne Benjamin (Penguin, 1985) is his wife's account of their struggle.

Other books that will help you understand something of the African experience are:
 Tell Freedom, Peter Abrahams (Faber and Faber, 1982)
 A Walk in the Night and Other Stories, Alex le Guma (Heinemann African Writers Series, 1968)

Stench of Kerosene
by Amrita Pritam

Working with the story

1 Find at least three details in the opening passage which show that Guleri looked forward to her visit home.

2 Explain the special meaning that the fair has for Manak.

3 In what ways would you say Manak and Guleri have:
● followed tradition
● broken with customs
in their courtship and subsequent marriage?

4 Read carefully the following lines as they appear in the story:

'Cattle go for unripe corn . . . . Human beings prefer it roasted. If you want me, go and ask my father for my hand.' (p. 23)

Explain what Guleri means by this.

5 What clues have you picked up about Manak's mother and her views? Using words she might use, explain her plans for her son's happiness.

6 Trace Manak's feelings as they are revealed to us in the story. Explain how you as a reader respond to his part in the events.

Reading between the lines

1 Write the letter that Guleri sends to Manak on the first occasion when she goes back home to visit her family.

2 Working in pairs, role-play a discussion between Manak and his mother in which he tells her of his intention to get married. Then role-play a further conversation where the question of a second marriage is brought up.

Leaving the story behind

1 This story deals with the difficult question of love matches versus arranged marriages. It is easy for Western societies to dismiss arranged marriages as oppressive. Consider the arguments which might be used to defend or attack both traditions and then write an essay setting out the merits and difficulties associated with each form of courtship and marriage.

2 Research the marriage traditions of another culture from that of your own and write about a ceremony that appeals to you, or describe a wedding that you have recently attended. You can include photographs to illustrate your writing or perhaps describe the wedding as if you were looking at a series of photographs.

3 Many stories have been written about the difficulties experienced by young lovers whose families come from different social or racial groups. You may have already seen, or studied *Romeo and Juliet*, *West Side Story* or *The Outsiders*. In pairs, write a conversation between a young person and a parent who disapproves of his or her relationship.

Wider reading

The contrasts and conflicts between different cultures or societies are explored in these books we have suggested for further reading:

The Outsiders, S. E. Hinton, (Macmillan, 1989)

Roll of Thunder, Hear My Cry, Mildred D. Taylor (New Windmill, 1987)

Basketball Game, Julius Lester (Puffin Plus, 1988)

Untouchable Orient, Mulk Raj Anand (New Delhi, 1970)

Stories from Pakistan and Bangladesh, Ranjana Ash (Harrap, 1980)

Sumitra's Story, Rukshana Smith (Bodley Head, 1982: Macmillan, 1985)

Cry, the Peacock, Anita Desai (Orient Paperbacks, 1983)

Snowdrops
by Leslie Norris

Working with the story

1 As you read the story you will gradually become aware that it is being presented from the viewpoint of a small boy. What details in the first two paragraphs of the story help the reader to see things through the boy's eyes?

2 What impression has Edmund made on the boy? Why do you think he has chosen him as his best friend?

3 Note down the changes in the usual routine of the school.
   • What do they tell the reader about Miss Webster's feelings?
   • How does the boy interpret the changes she makes to their day?

4 Look at the details that suggest that the story has a Welsh setting. What impression do you get of the community and its way of life? Do you think this is important to your understanding of the story?

5 Flowers are frequently used as emblems or symbols of deep feelings about death as well as about courtship and marriage.
   • How are the snowdrops used to underline the central themes of the story?
   • What connections can a reader make between the flower, the young teacher, a funeral and the boy's day in school.

6 Reread the last sentence of the story again. How effective do you find this ending?

Reading between the lines

1 Write the boy's diary entry for this day, giving his view of what happened. Then write Miss Webster's diary entry for the day, describing her feelings and experiences.

Leaving the story behind

1 Rewrite this story as a radio play remembering that all the clues about the events of the story will have to come through the dialogue or by the use of convincing sound effects.

2 Consider the way in which Leslie Norris shows that his main character fails to understand Miss Webster's feelings. Write a story about family problems from the viewpoint of a young child. Try to

make the reader aware of situations that the child only partly understands.

3   Look again at question 5 of 'Working with the story'. Then write your own short story or poem concerned with loss or growing up. Use a flower as a symbol of the feelings involved and give a description of the flower at important moments in the story.

4   Reread the conversation between the boy and Edmund (p. 30) with a partner. Discuss the sort of things that are important in their lives. Share your memories of playground conversations and games. Use your childhood memories or observations of young children to write a short dialogue between two or three children in a school playground.

5   If the story reminds you of your own primary school days begin to write up the incidents as work towards a final autobiography. Leave your stories as separate anecdotes to form part of your autobiographical fragments.

Wider reading

'Snowdrops' is taken from Leslie Norris's collection, *Sliding* (Longman, 1978).

Related reading
Stories which deal with the difficulties of growing up include:
    'Through the Tunnel', Doris Lessing and 'Message from the Pigman', John Wain in *Short Stories of Our Time*, ed. Douglas Barnes (Harrap, 1963)
    'My Oedipus Complex' in *My Oedipus Complex and Other Stories*, Frank O'Connor (Penguin, 1984)

For stories dealing with children's perspectives on events, try:
    'World's End' from *World's End and Other Stories*, Paul Theroux, (Penguin, 1982)
    'Should Wizard Hit Mommy' from *Pigeon Feathers and Other Stories*, John Updike (Andre Deutsch, 1968)

The Fly-paper

by Elizabeth Taylor

Working with the story

1 Before you read the story, write down any ideas that are suggested to you by the title. You should think about the role usually played by flies in rhymes and stories. Try to predict what the story might be about before you begin reading. Note this down so that you can compare your preliminary ideas with your final response.

2 The music teacher's room is described as a 'darkened parlour'. Using this as your starting point, pick out other ways in which the writer creates a sense of foreboding. How do these images affect you as a reader?

3 As the story unfolds, we learn more about Sylvia and the way she has been brought up. What are your own feelings about her upbringing and her attitude to adults?

4 The woman on the bus looks 'sharply' at the man when he begins to sing to Sylvia.
- How did you first interpret her stare?
- How does your interpretation change when you have read the whole story?

5 Explain how the writer shows you that Sylvia is willing to trust the woman.

6 What atmosphere is created by the description of the woman's kitchen? How is this impression altered by the introduction of the fly-paper?

7 What are your feelings at the end of the story?

Reading between the lines

1 Design a cover for a paperback edition of a short story anthology containing 'The Fly-paper'. You will need to choose an image that suggests Sylvia's plight. You may include a caption which sums up the action of the story.

2 Imagine you are Sylvia writing your diary before going to the music lesson with Mrs Harrison. Write down your feelings about going to the lessons and the journey there.

112

Leaving the story behind

1 The story may have reminded you of the 'horror' of being forced to attend various activities like Sunday School, ballet lessons or Cubs.

Either write an account of your own journey to the activity; include your thoughts and feelings about the ordeal to come.

Or write about one or two activities in separate anecdotes that can form part of your autobiographical fragments.

2 Read some of the stories we have recommended in the 'Wider reading' section to see how other writers have created suspense within their stories. Write a story with a final twist at the end; you need only hint at the final horror, but you will need to leave sufficient clues in the story for your reader to be able to guess the ending.

3 Some readers have enjoyed writing parodies of this story in which a suggested threat turns out to be something ridiculously harmless. One such story involved a milkman being terrified by the threat of little demons in what appeared from the description to be an enormous spooky house. The story ended by revealing that the man was delivering milk to a primary school. Write your own parody of a 'chiller' story.

4 There has been a lot of publicity about alerting small children to the possible dangers from grown-ups. Collect any information from the library, the NSPCC, Childline or local agencies on this subject.

Imagine that a local primary school has asked you to create a display and some activities to help infant children to understand about the possible danger from strangers. Choose from the following activities:

- colouring exercises
- a poster
- classroom games
- a booklet
- a tape slide production with a teacher's guide
- your own idea

Write a letter to accompany your project, addressed to the head teacher, explaining the materials you have designed and how you would like them to be used. When designing your materials you will need to think very carefully about your audience's needs. You will need to think particularly carefully about the kind of language appropriate to a young audience and the balance between pictures and written information. Look at other materials written specifically for younger children to help you.

113

Wider reading

'The Landlady' and 'Lamb to the Slaughter' by Roald Dahl in *Tales of the Unexpected* (Penguin, 1979) are particularly effective examples of stories with a final twist at the end.

For the work of another writer who uses shock tactics try reading: 'Marionettes Inc.' and 'The Murderer' from *The Stories of Ray Bradbury* Vol 1, (Grafton, 1983).

Related reading
'Sweets from a Stranger', Nicholas Fisk (Puffin, 1990) deals with the theme of child abduction in a very different way.

'Uncle Ernest', John Wain in *Short Stories of our Time*, ed. Douglas Barnes, gives us the other side of the picture; a lonely old man in search of company.

Jane is a Girl
by Walter Macken

Working with the story

1   Jot down your response to the title of this story and compare your ideas with those of others in the class. What ideas for a story does it suggest?

2   Write down your first impressions of Jude and the place he occupies in his family.

3   Which details in this story suggest it has an Irish setting? What impression have you formed of the neighbourhood and the people who live there?

4   In what ways does the writer build up a sense of increasing excitement in the description of the hurley game?

5   What effect does Jude's discovery about Jane have on the way he behaves and the way he reacts to the others?

6   Jude wonders whether Jane felt the same, whether she said, why Jude is a boy (p. 47). What do you think?

Reading between the lines

1   Both this story and the story titled 'Snowdrops' focus upon important moments in growing up. Identify the key moments in

114

each story and explain their effect on you as a reader. Compare your choice of moments with those of a friend and discuss any differences in your choices.

2 Draw a story board to bring out the key moments in the game of hurley. Use close up shots to establish your main characters and to focus on important details like the bag of sweets and long shots to establish the setting and the scope of the game.

Leaving the story behind

1 Describe any game or special activity which you shared with a group of friends. Concentrate on giving your audience a clear account of the way you organised yourself and the different roles involved. Talk about a particular game in as vivid and detailed a way as you can explaining any specialist vocabulary or equipment.

2 Choose a game that you are familiar with and that you think will appeal to other young people. Write a set of instructions for the game. Concentrate on making your instructions easy to follow and unambiguous.

3 Look back on your own childhood and draw a timeline, marking off key events in your life. Set it out like the one below:

HAPPINESS

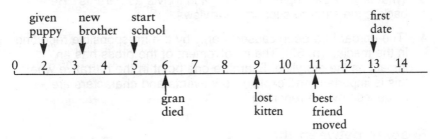

UNHAPPINESS

Use the timeline to identify a time in your life when an important change occurred. Write an account of this change for your autobiographical fragments and try to include the reactions of other members of your family to it. If you prefer to, write short pieces about one or two incidents.

Wider reading

Some other stories which deal with key moments in childhood and growing up are:

'The Kiss', by Walter Macken in *Coll Doll* (Pan, 1976).
Nobody's Family is Going to Change, Louis Fitzhugh (Armada Lions, 1981)
'The End of Something', from *The Snows of Kilimanjaro*, Ernest Hemingway (Penguin, 1964)
The Friends, Rosa Guy, (Macmillan, 1982)
A Solitary Blue, Cynthia Voight (Collins, 1986)

Don: The True Story of a Young Person

by Garrison Keillor

Working with the story

1   What evidence is there in the story to show that Don and his parents care about each other?

2   What fears do Don's parents have about his life style?

3   What is your own opinion of Earl and Mavis as parents? Refer back to the story to support your views.

4   'The uproar had been caused partly by the irresponsible reporting in the media,' (p. 53). The involvement of the press has an impact on the storyline. Examine one point in the narrative where this is important and explain how events and characters are influenced by the reporting.

Reading between the lines

1   Write the newspaper story: 'RIOT AS ROCK BAND EATS LIVE CHICKEN' Set it out as it would appear on the front page of a tabloid newspaper.

2   Make a list of the kind of behaviour disliked by Mrs Goodrich and the Committee for Teen Decency. Draw up the Committee's ten point plan to re-establish decency. Before you begin you will need to define what the group understands by the word, *decency* and think what action it would like to take.

3 *Either* write a press release for the Trash's forthcoming Tampa Tour. Include descriptions of their songs, information about group members and their previous 'successful' appearances.

Or in small groups, role-play a press conference for Trash. You will need a publicity manager as well as members of the group and representatives from the media.

Leaving the story behind

1 Differences between parents and children are common. Drawing from your own experiences and those of your friends write about the generation gap.

2 Don's lyrics reflect his particular beliefs and values. Write the lyrics for your own songs which reflect your beliefs and values. You could present these lyrics as part of a record sleeve which you have designed for your first album.

3 How are young people presented in the media? In groups, analyse a week's editions of newspapers and magazines. Cut out all the stories related to young people and mount an annotated display showing favourable, unfavourable or neutral images.

- Which images are most prevalent?
- Are young men and women given equal coverage, similar treatment?

Present your findings on the images of youth to the class as an illustrated talk using the display and any other visual aids that seem appropriate.

Wider reading

This story is taken from a collection by Garrison Keillor called *Happy to Be Here*. The author is better known for *Lake Wobegon Days*, his description of life in a small Mid-Western American town (Faber, 1985). You may find many of the ideas in this book difficult, but it is worth dipping into for his humorous accounts of growing up in this kind of environment. Look, for instance, at the account of registering to go to college on pp. 152–166, where he gives his opinions about the members of his family.

Related reading

Points of Departure, Six Women Remember Their Early Lives, ed. Jane Browne (Students' Virago, 1988) is an excellent introduction to constraints on the lives of young women.

117

'Shot Actress, Full Story' by H. E. Bates in *Short Stories of Our Time* ed. D. Barnes (Harrap, 1963) deals with the unscrupulous behaviour of the press.

'Nineteen Fiftyfive', in *You Can't Keep a Good Woman Down* by Alice Walker (Women's Press, 1982), picks up the theme of the black origins of pop music.

A Piece of Pie
by Damon Runyon

Working with the story

1 In small groups, begin by trying to read some of the story out loud. As you read the story try to picture the characters and pay particular attention to the tone of voice they might use.

2 Pick out examples of the slang used in this particular story and explain the humour it creates.

3 Write a glossary of the unusual idioms used by the characters. Make a list of some of your own slang terms and give explanations of what they mean and when you would use them.

4 The names of the characters are important clues to their personalities. List the names used in the story and explain how they fit the person described.

5 This story is written as if a member of the group, present at the event but not directly involved, is telling the story.

● What effect does this have on you as you read?
● What attitude does the narrator take to the characters he presents to the reader?

Reading between the lines

1 Adapt a short scene from this story for an English audience, setting it in an area you know about, the East End of London, South Yorkshire or Liverpool, perhaps. Use appropriate dialect, names and types of food for the contest.

2 *Either* imagine a local radio station is covering the eating contest. Plan the broadcast to include interviews with the contestants and their supporters before and after the match. Remember to distinguish between the interviewer and the presenter of the programme

- The interviewer can ask questions before the event, speculating on the outcome and, after the result, congratulating the winner, or sympathising with the other contestants.
- The presenter needs to give a clear account of the competition, supplying additional information about the contestants where appropriate.

Or write a script for the eating contest scene as part of a play. If you intend to produce the play for TV use a story board to direct the camera shots. This should consist of a series of framed pictures with details of the kind of shot you require. Use close-ups to establish your characters and long shots to create the setting.

Leaving the story behind

1 Stories about bets or contests where one character outwits another are very popular. They can be traced back to the earliest tales such as Aesop's *Fables* or Chaucer's *Canterbury Tales* and they still feature today in cartoons and films. Pool ideas about similar stories you have encountered and write your own updated version using contemporary slang, names and situations.

2 Write a story which is based on food and the pleasures (or pains) of eating.

3 Write about any contests or competitions you have taken part in for your autobiographical fragments.

Wider reading

More of this writer's stories can be found in *Runyon on Broadway: a Runyon Omnibus* (Constable, 1953).

Related reading
Other humorous stories you might enjoy are:
Alan Coren's 'Arthur' stories, for example, 'Lone Arthur' (Robson Books, 1978)
Vintage Thurber (Penguin, 1982)
Revolting Rhymes, Roald Dahl (Puffin, 1984)

'The Great Leapfrog Contest' by William Saroyan in *The Trouble with Tigers* (Harcourt, Brace, 1938) is a story about quite a different competition.

Gorilla, My Love
by Toni Cade Bambara

Working with the story

1   Like the last story, 'A Piece of Pie', this is a story narrated by
    someone with a distinctive way of talking and writing. You will
    probably understand it better if you read it out aloud to each other
    in groups.

2   Make a note of any words and phrases that you found difficult to
    understand on first reading. Write down what you supposed
    them to mean, using the context to guide you. In small groups,
    compare your definitions and devise a glossary of terms which
    you think would help someone reading the story for the first time.

3   Choose parts of the story that are not written in standard English
    and rewrite them in a more formal way. Set your work out like
    this:

Page	Story Version	Standard English Version
79	I don't feature sittin in the back	You wouldn't find me in the back of the car
79	which suit me just fine	This suited me very well *or* I liked this a lot
81	grownups messin over kids	grown-ups treating children badly

In pairs, share your new versions and talk about what differences
it would make to the story if it was written in standard English.
(Think about your impression of the main character, the credibility
of the conversation and the pace of the story.)

4   How does the way the story is written support the things that
    Hazel tells us about herself? Look particularly at the way she links
    ideas and begins her sentences, as well as her use of dialect and
    slang terms.

5   List the different names that are given to Hazel in the story and
    comment on what they tell us about her character and
    relationships with others.

6 Why was the visit to the cinema such a disappointment to Hazel and her brothers? Why do you think they reacted so strongly against the film they were shown?

7 The title, 'Gorilla, My Love', is the name of the film that the narrator hoped to see with her brothers.
- What expectations did the title create for them?
- Why do you think it has been chosen for the title of the whole story?

8 This story first appeared under the title 'I ain't Playin, I'm Hurtin'. Which title do you prefer and why? You will need to think of the expectations created by each title.

Reading between the lines

1 In the course of the story we learn a lot about Hazel and her attitude to authority. Use the information to write a report about her as if you were her school teacher.

2 Write the conversation that you imagine Hazel has with her father when he finds out about the cinema escapade from Big Brood.

3 Write a letter of complaint about the children from the cinema's manager to their parents.

Leaving the story behind

1 Write about any memorable experiences of going to the cinema as part of your autobiographical fragments.

2 Write your own piece about a disappointment or broken promise, or a time when adults failed to live up to your expectations.

3 Review any work you did on names after reading the first story in the collection. Read the opening lines of a poem written by Marge Piercy about her name, 'If I had been called Sabrina or Ann, she said':

> I'm the only poet with the name.
> Can you imagine a ballerina named
> Marge? Marge Curie, Nobel Prize winner.
> Empress Marge. My lady Marge? Rhymes with
> large/charge/barge . . .

Write a similar poem about your own name, or one for Hazel, the main character in this story.

Wider reading

This story is taken from a collection of the same name, Gorilla, My Love (Women's Press, 1972). You might also like to try her other volume of short stories, *The Sea Birds Are Still Alive* (Women's Press, 1982).

Related reading

'Frankie Mae', Jean Wheeler Smith, in *Frankie Mae and Other Stories*, ed. Ann Mann and Hilary Rich (Nelson Responses Series, 1987)

A Visit from the Footbinder, Emily Prager (Chatto and Windus, 1983)

The Friends, Rosa Guy, (Macmillan, 1982)

Other stories about growing up that may interest you are:
  To Kill A Mocking Bird, Harper Lee (Macmillan, 1987)
  If it Weren't for Sebastian, Jean Ure (Puffin Plus, 1988)

Rapunzstiltskin

by Liz Lochhead

Working with the story

1 This poem is based on two fairy stories, Rapunzel and Rumplestiltskin. Sort out in two columns which lines belong to which story. You may need to read the original stories in a collection of fairy tales.

2 Liz Lochhead deliberately uses clichés. Clichés are words or phrases that have been used so often they have become ‾unoriginal and flat. List the ones she uses and explain why she uses them and what effect they have on the poem.

3 What impression does the prince make on the heroine in the poem? Is this the way that princes are expected to behave? How do princes behave in the stories you know? Give particular examples.

Reading between the lines

1 In what ways has Liz Lochhead challenged the expectations that readers usually bring to fairy stories or folk tales? Why has she done this do you think?

You may find it easier to organise your answer in the form of a chart:

Traditional fairy story	This version
The prince is brave and comes to the heroine's rescue.	The prince is stupid and the princess does not want to be rescued.
The princess is helpless.	The princess does all the hard work and has to give the prince instructions.

Leaving the story behind

1 *Either* write your own fairy tale combining two or more well-known stories in a way that changes their meaning.

Or write an update of a fairy story which questions some of the accepted conventions. For example, you might include a prince on a motorbike, a heroine working at a supermarket checkout, a wolf who is a landlord. Sometimes a special item taken from a fairy story will help you to focus your writing, like a pair of red shoes, a spinning wheel, or a mechanical nightingale.

2 Read a selection of popular fairy stories. Prepare a report for parents which highlights the possible stereotypes of male and female behaviour which these stories present. You may wish to consider the following points:

● How are princes and princesses expected to behave?
● Who shows initiative in the story?
● Are there other sex-role stereotypes, for example, witches or wicked step-mothers, ogres or wicked uncles?

You may wish to develop this work further by doing a survey of the representation of masculine and feminine roles in either fairy stories or children's books.

In small groups, collect together a selection of six to eight books aimed at early readers. Try to include some published after 1980. Analyse the contents to see how masculine and feminine characters are presented. Use the following table to categorise the roles:

Type of activity	Male characters	Female characters
Jobs/Professions		
Work in and around the home		
Hobbies/Games		
Getting into trouble		

- Are there any noticeable differences between the books published before 1980 and those published after that date?
- Are there any other features about the characters in the book that struck you? Consider the kind of homes they live in; the families that are shown and their cultural backgrounds.
- Are there any conclusions that you can draw about the way in which the world is presented to young readers?

Present your group's findings to the rest of the class.

3 Write about the fairy stories you read as a child for your autobiography.

Wider reading

Alternative versions of fairy tales can be found in the following collections:

Dreaming Frankenstein and Collected Poems, Liz Lochhead (Polygon, 1986)

The Practical Princess and Other Liberating Fairy Tales, Jay Williams (Macmillan Educational, 1986)

Clever Gretchen and Other Forgotten Folk Tales, Alison Lurie, (Heinemann, 1980)

Revolting Rhymes, Roald Dahl (Puffin, 1984)

The Glass Cupboard
by Terry Jones

Working with the story

1 Read the opening paragraphs and predict what kind of story you imagine it will be. Write down the reasons for your prediction.

2 With a partner, make a list of the elements in this story that belong to traditional ways of telling fairy tales. Think about the way the story is told, its beginning and ending, as well as the setting and the characters.

Reading between the lines

1 'The Glass Cupboard' has a moral to it. Explain what that moral is. Think of an illustration which would convey the message to a reader.

Leaving the story behind

1 *Either* prepare a dramatised reading of the story which would be suitable to present to primary school children.

   Or write the story as a play for a younger age group. You will need to think very carefully how you will turn the action into dialogue so that the audience understand all the implications.

2 Read some of the fairy stories recommended in the 'Wider reading' list. Write your own fable warning against a contemporary danger, the destruction of wildlife, for example, or the erosion of the ozone layer.

3 *Either* research one aspect of conservation (for example, saving an endangered species) using your school and the local library for information and by writing to conservation groups for leaflets and other publicity materials. Present your views on the topic to the class using any visual aids you can acquire.

   Or using information you have collected on a particular issue, prepare a pamphlet. Specify the audience for your material and be careful to use language that is appropriate to that group.

Wider reading

There are many collections of fairy stories to choose from. Some with the same kind of moral purpose include:

The Happy Prince and Other Stories, Oscar Wilde (Puffin, 1985)
How the Whale Became and Other Stories, Ted Hughes (Puffin, 1971)
More English Fairy Tales, David Nutt (1984)
Don't Bet on the Prince, Jack Zipes (Gower Publishing Company, 1986)

The Day They Burned the Books

by *Jean Rhys*

Working with the story

1 The story is set in the Caribbean and is told from the point of view of one of the children involved. What does she tell us about her background and family? How does this differ from that of her friend, Eddie Sawyer?

2 Why did the behaviour of Mr Sawyer puzzle other people? What does this tell you about the society on the island?

3 What do you learn about the marriage of the Sawyers in the story? Think about the incident when Mr Sawyer pulls his wife's hair. For whom do you feel most sympathy and why?

4 The storyteller is called a 'colonial' by English children; what do you understand by this name, and in what ways does it explain her beliefs about England?

5 Is the death of Eddie's father presented in the story as a tragic event? Give reasons for your answer.

6 Why do you think Mrs Sawyer gets rid of the books?

7 When Eddie tries to stop his mother burning one of the books he says, 'Now I've got to hate you too.' Why does he say this?

8 At the end of the story the narrator wants to read the book she has taken. Why is this book so important to her?

Reading between the lines

1 In pairs, role-play the scene where Eddie discovers his mother burning his father's books. You will need to discuss the reasons Mrs Sawyer gives for her actions and the reasons for Eddie's distress. Present your scene to the class.

126

2 Imagine that Eddie and the narrator have kept a diary recording their friendship and their thoughts and feelings about each other's family.

- Write a page from each diary which compares their views. You may want to choose a particular incident or focus on a particular character.

Leaving the story behind

1 Write your own story about a close friendship between people from different racial backgrounds, though not necessarily between a boy and girl.

2 For your autobiographical fragments, write about any experiences of prejudice or discrimination you have experienced or witnessed.

Wider reading

This story is taken from a collection of Jean Rhys' stories called *Tales from the Caribbean*, in which you will find descriptions of the islands and the people.

Related reading
   Green Days by the River, Michael Antony (Heinemann, 1973) provides opportunities to read about life in Trinidad in the 1950s.
   Try some of these too:
   Caribbean Stories, ed. Michael Marland (Longman, 1978)
   Best West Indian Stories, Kenneth Ramchand (Nelson, 1982)
   My Love, My Love, Rosa Guy, ed. Stella Canwell (Student's Virago, 1988)
   The Friends, Rosa Guy, (Macmillan, 1982)
   Black Lives White Worlds, Keith Ajegbo (CUP, 1982)

■ WORKING WITH THE ANTHOLOGY ■

When you have read several stories in this anthology you will begin to appreciate some of the ideas and ways of writing that link them. The next four activities will help you to make your own links between stories in the anthology in preparation for the assignments that follow.

1 Working in small groups make a chart of the thematic links between the stories. You may wish to use some of the following suggestions, adding your own categories to them:

Theme	Story
Growing up	'Snowdrops'; 'Jane is a Girl'; 'The Day They Burned the Books'
Conflict or lack of communication between cultures	'Everyday Use'; 'A Chip of Glass Ruby'; 'Stench of Kerosene';
Conflict across generations	'Gorilla, My Love'; 'Jane is a Girl'; 'Snowdrops'
Speaking Out	
Woman's role	
Names and identity	
Different ways of talking/telling	
Parent/child relationships	
Boy/girl relationships	

2 Another way in which you may wish to categorise the stories is to look at the genre or type of story they represent. Here are some suggestions to start you off:

Genre	Examples
Anecdote with a strong twist at the end	'The Fly-paper'; 'Stench of Kerosene'
A small slice of life	
A character study	
First person narrative	
Moral tale or fairy story	
A dramatic incident that encapsulates an important issue	

3 In pairs, prepare an analysis sheet like the one that follows for each of the stories.

Short story analysis sheet

Title (include your first response to it) ....
....
....

Author (nationality; when written etc.)..
....
....

Background/setting (e.g. period, location, time span)..................................
....
....

Central character(s) (sex, age, occupation)..
....
....

Impression of character (hero/heroine/anti-hero)..............................
....
....

Other significant character(s) (sex, age, occupation) ....
....
....

Impression of character (lover, villian, helper, opponent)..................
....
....

Narrator (age, sex, occupation, attitude etc.)..............................
....
....

Role in the story (participant/observer; point of view) ....
....
....

Situation presented..
....
....

Resolution (happy ending/twist/moral)..
....
....

Genre (e.g. thriller, fairy tale, character study, comedy) ....
....
....

Similarities with other stories..
....
....

Personal response ....
....
....

Use the information gained from completing the charts and analysis sheets to tackle the following questions.

1 Choose two or three stories with a common theme or narrative style and compare and contrast them, showing clearly which of the stories you preferred.

2 Some of the stories are humorous in their presentation of characters or events. Look back at those stories that you found most amusing and analyse the ways in which the writers created that humour.

3 Several of the stories can be described as having a moral purpose or a social message. Which stories do you think fit this category? Describe the story which you have found most effective in challenging, changing or confirming your own opinions and beliefs.

4 Which kind of story have you enjoyed reading most? Write a review of the story you have found most rewarding.

5 Which of the stories do you think aroused the most interest in its storyteller? How was this achieved? Try to write your own story using a character other than yourself as narrator.

The hot seat

Work in groups of about six. One person should adopt the role of a character in a particular story. The rest of the group need to prepare questions. Each group should present its question and answer session to the whole class and one of the group should prepare an introduction to the 'guest' in the hot seat.

Suggestions

1 New York journalists question Dee from 'Everyday Use' about her lifestyle and her roots in her family's past.

2 Mr Bamjee from 'A Chip of Glass Ruby' is questioned about his wife's political activities and his own attitudes to them.

3 The King in 'The Glass Cupboard' faces interrogation by the media on the dangers to the environment occasioned by the loss of the cupboard.

4 Manak's mother from 'Stench of Kerosene' is questioned by other members of her family and village about his marriages and the circumstances surrounding the death of Guleri.

5 Hazel from 'Gorilla, My Love' is questioned about her part in the upset in the cinema.

6   Nicely-Nicely Jones from 'A Piece of Pie' is questioned about his
    abilities as a champion eater and his prospects in the eating
    contest.

Activity map

The following map relates the stories in the anthology to the kind of written and group tasks we have suggested you might like to choose.

EVERYDAY USE: ACTIVITY MAP

Story	Page	Kinds of writing	Other activities suggested
Everyday Use	1	Character study Point of view Personal writing Poem Autobiographical fragment	Group work/ presentation Considering names
A Chip of Glass Ruby	11	Character Study Persuasive writing Designing a leaflet Discursive essay Letter to a newspaper Journalism	Background research Writing and delivering a speech

Stench of Kerosene	21	Character study Point of view Dialogue Short story Discursive essay Letter Autobiographical fragment	Background research
Snowdrops	27	Point of view Dialogue Radio script Dialogue Autobiographical fragment	Looking at symbolism
The Fly-paper	35	Publicity campaign Parody Personal writing Narrative Autobiographical fragment	Prediction Designing a book cover
Jane is a Girl	43	Comparison with "Snowdrops" Point of view Writing instructions Descriptive writing Autobiographical fragments	Timeline Storyboard

Story	Page	Kinds of writing	Other activities suggested
Don: the True Story of a Young Person	49	Journalism Publicity/advertising Press release Discursive essay Lyrics	Analysing media images Roe-play
A Piece of Pie	63	Journalism Personal writing Descriptive writing Looking at humour Autobiographical fragment Rewriting story for a different audience	Looking at language Conducting interviews Storyboards
Gorilla, My Love	78	Dialogue Letter of complaint Film review Autobiographical fragment Poem	Looking at standard English Storyboard
Rapunzstiltskin	85	Rewriting fairy stories Discursive essay	Genre work Analysing children's stories Looking at stereotyping
The Glass Cupboard	88	Fairy story Play script	Dramatised reading

The Day They Burned the Books	92	Book reviews Writing for children	Character study Diaries Autobiographical fragment	